MODERN GUIDE

TO

PROFESSIONAL GAMEKEEPING

OTHER TITLES AVAILABLE OR IN PREPARATION

FIELD SPORTS

The Notorious Poacher by G. Bedson

Shotgun Shooting by John Brindle

High Pheasants in Theory and Practice by Sir Ralph F. Payne-Gallway, Bt.

Stag Hunting on Exmoor with The Devon & Somerset Staghounds by Malcolm C. McGowan (A Special Edition is also available)

Way of the Gamekeeper by J. Mason

The Gamekeeper at Home - Richard Jefferies. The Artist's Edition: A Classic Reprint (limp)

Ferrets and Ferreting - W. Carnegie (limp)

The Shotgun and Its Uses - E. Sussex

Legal Aspects of Field Sports - J. Mason (limp)

PHEASANTS AND WATERFOWL

Pheasants and Their Enemies by Dr. J. O'C. Fitzsimmons (limp)

Pheasants of the World by Jean Delacour

Fancy Waterfowl by F. Finn

MODERN GUIDE

TO

PROFESSIONAL

GAMEKEEPING

by
J. MASON
Professional Gamekeeper

Published by:
NIMROD PRESS LTD.,
15 The Maltings,
Turk Street,
Alton,
Hampshire GU34 1DL

© J. Mason and Nimrod Press Ltd., 1989

This book is copyright and may not be reproduced in whole
or in part (except for review) without the express
permission of the publishers in writing

First Published 1989'

ISBN 1-85259-060-2

Typeset by Betagraphics, The King's House, Bow Street, Langport
Somerset TA10 9PS

Ptarmigan Printing

NIMROD PRESS LTD.
15 The Maltings
Turk Street,
Alton, Hants, GU34 1DL

CHAPTER		PAGE

1	Gamekeeping Today	1
2	The Pheasant keeper's year	13
3	Vermin Control and Hazards to Game	29
4	Egg Production and Incubation	69
5	Rearing	93
6	Releasing Birds	121
7	Woodland release pens and cover crops	137
8	Diseases	155
9	Poaching	169
10	Wild Partridge	175
11	Grouse	189
12	Wildfowl	203
13	River Keeping	215
14	Deer Control	231
15	Firearms	247
16	Ferreting	265
17	Dogs	273
18	Legal Aspects of Field Sports	299
19	Do's and Don't s Out Shooting	339
20	Glossary of Abbreviations, Shooting Terms and Others	347
	Index	363

LIST OF ILLUSTRATIONS

1.1	The Gamekeeper	2
2.1	Game for the Table	14
2.2	Cock Pheasant	16
2.3	Woodcock Shooting	18
2.4	Natural Food for Pheasants	20
2.5	Reared Pheasants	20
2.6	The Original Game Cart	23
2.7	A Feed "Steddle"	24
2.8	Cock Pheasant	27
2.9	Pheasant Flushing	28
3.1	Various Winged Vermin	30
3.2	Sparrow Hawk Feeding Young	32
3.3	The Fox	34
3.4	Predators of Game	36
3.5	Identification of Tracks	37
3.6	Badger Sets	39
3.7	The Badger	39
3.8	Fox Snares	41
3.9	Gin Traps	41
3.10	Stoat in Fenn Trap and Empty	43
3.11	Cage Traps for Birds	44
3.12	Traps on Rafts	45
3.13	Tunnel of Dead Wood	45
3.14	Pigeon Decoys	48
3.15	Night Shooting Rabbits	54
3.16	Traps - Mink and Mole Traps	58
3.17	Traps	62
3.18	Pump - Motorised	65
3.19	Cymag Hand Pump	65
4.1	Drop Catcher	70
4.2	Wire-Netting Catcher	70
4.3	Walled Garden	73

4.4	Laying Pens	73
4.5	English Partridges	74
4.6	French Partridges	74
4.7	"Rotomaid" Egg Washer	77
4.8	"Papier Mache" Egg Trays	77
4.9	Hygienic Storage Trays	80
4.10	Plastic Inserts	81
4.11	An "Ironclad" Still Air Incubator	81
4.12	A large Cabinet Incubator	83
4.13	A Western Incubator	83
4.15	Egg Candling	85
4.16	Stages in Hatching	88
4.17	Typical Traps	90
4.18	Tethered Hens	90
4.19	Bristol Incubator	92
4.20	Bristol Hatcher	92
5.1	Box for Chicks	94
5.2	Day old Chicks	96
5.3	Partridge and Pheasant Chicks	96
5.4	Young Chicks - Rearing	100
5.5	A large scale rearing enterprise	101
5.6	Conventional rearing system	101
5.7	A 500-chick size (Hardwick)	102
5.8	Large circular Brooder	103
5.9	Rubert type	103
5.10	Automatic Drinker	106
5.11	Tube Feeders	106
5.12	Interior of Brooder House	107
5.12	Ducklings being released	107
5.14	40 gallon container: Food Hopper	108
5.15	Gaybird type Gas Heater	108
5.16	Good quality feed	109
5.17	Automatic Drinker	109
5.18	Original Paraffin model	113
5.19	English Partridge chicks	113
5.20	Existing buildings	116

5.21	Bristol Electric Hen	119
6.1	Automatic Feeders	123
6.2	Feed Hoppers	125
6.3	Wheat Dispenser	125
6.4	Healthy Poults	127
6.5	Straw for Pheasants	127
6.6	French Partridge	129
6.7	Partridges on a January morning	130
6.8	Mallard Ducks	133
6.9	Pheasant Poult crate	135
6.10	Wing tags and pliers	135
6.11	Pheasant Poults flying	136
7.1	Woodland	138
7.2	A useful wood with Game cover	140
7.3	Wood sheltered by shrubs	140
7.4	Drives from sugar beet	142
7.5	Failed crop, but still a useful drive	142
7.6	Mustard grown as camouflage	144
7.7	Stubble burning	144
7.8	Release Pens	146
7.9	Favourite meal of Maize cobs	146
7.10	Sewelling	147
7.11	Low bushes needed in release pen	147
9.1	Lurchers	170
9.2	A sitting Target	170
9.3	Alarm Gun	174
10.1	Grey or English Partridge	176
10.2	Hybrid French or Red-legged Partridge	176
10.3	Uncovered French Nest	181
10.4	Exposed Nest	181
10.5	Very small day old Chick	183
10.6	Broody Bantams	183
10.7	Overgrown hedge	186
10.8	Partridge shooting country	186
10.9	Partridge shooting in late September	188
11.1	Grouse on the Moor	190

11.2	Ptarmigan	192
11.3	Black Grouse (Blackcock)	192
11.4	Heather burning	195
11.5	Grouse are very territorial	195
11.6	Mosaic moorland	197
11.7	Grouse Butts	197
11.8	Beaters	200
11.9	A "Gun's Eye View"	200
12.1	Canada Geese	204
12.2	Greylag Geese	204
12.3	Mallard	206
12.4	Wigeon	206
12.5	Wildfowling country	209
12.6	Secluded flight ponds	209
12.7	Well hidden duck hides	209
13.1	Species of game fish	217
13.2	Boats for reed cutting	221
13.3	Pike	221
13.4	A Hampshire trout river	223
13.5	Fly fisher	225
13.6	Brightly coloured flies	225
13.7	Trout flies	227
13.8	A Dun insect	227
13.9	Stew Pounds	230
14.1	Sika Deer with antlers velvet	232
14.2	Fallow Deer	232
14.3	Roe Deer	234
14.4	Red Deer	234
14.5	Wounded Deer and Dog	235
14.6	Muntjac Deer bone formation	238
14.7	Small antlers and tusks	238
14.8	Deer Stalking	240
14.9	Dapple coated Deer	246
15.1	Cabinet for storing guns	248
15.2	Different types of guns	251
15.3	Punt gun and ram rod	264

15.4	Demonstration of Punt Gunning	264
16.1	Ferret handling	266
16.2	Rabbits here since Normans	268
16.3	Ferrets and Terriers to make friends	268
16.4	Electronic Ferret finder	271
16.5	Rabbits in awkward places	272
17.1	Retrievers	277
17.2	Spaniels	277
17.3	Hunter Pointer and Retriever	279
17.4	A Fell-type Terrier	279
17.5	Good Workers!	281
17.6	Puppies	283
17.8	Introduction to Game	285
17.9	Picking up Game	285
17.11	Dummies	287
17.12	A Field Trial	297
17.13	The Rottweiler (Guard Dog)	298
19.1	Beaters on the way to a Shoot	340
19.2	A Picker up with Birds and Dogs	

INTRODUCTION

I should like to dedicate this book to David, for it was he who introduced me to such a fascinating and challenging way of life and by example, taught me the ways of gamekeeping.

I sincerely hope that this book broadens the knowledge of those interested in the profession of the gamekeeper and others already marginally involved. I hope it offers an insight to the trials and tribulations, the dedication and the responsibilities the work entails. May it also lead to a fuller appreciation of a good keeper and the beneficial effect of his job upon the countryside.

My thanks go to the following individuals from whom I have gleaned knowledge of subjects I knew little about. Mr. Bryan Burrows on grouse, Mr. Ron Wilton on river keeping, a keeper in Norfolk on wild partridge and Mr. Jim Sims on guns. I should also like to extend my appreciation to the manufacturers who have so kindly sent me illustrations of their products for inclusion in this book. Thanks, too, for Sheena and her typewriter.

I was at first very dubious of my ability to tackle such a book as this. I fully realised that every keeper has his own method of doing things. Experience is gained from actually doing the work, not reading about it in books. Experienced keepers derive quicker and more effective ways, many of which have been handed from one generation to another. Most of these men are far better qualified than me to write a book on the subject, but unfortunately they are not the sort to put pen to paper.

My hope is that they do not find too much to criticise between the covers of this book. Some of their ways infringe on recent legislation, so I have not been able to include these. However, I have tried to include a general appreciation of all that may be involved. The British landscape is varied and the keeper's duties are very much influenced by local conditions that prevail. Some keepers spend the greatest part of their lives on one estate, while others choose to move around to face fresh challenges and acquire new skills.

May the standards and pride in the profession be maintained by future generations and may there always be a place in rural Britain for the gamekeeper.

The two main organisations that particularly deal with shooting are:

The Game Conservancy,
Fordingbridge,
Hampshire SP6 1EF.

B.A.S.C. (British Association for Shooting and Conservation),
Marford Hill,
Rossett,
Clwyd LL12 0HL.

Numerous schemes and courses are organised by both these organisations. Advisory publications are also available to cover nearly every aspect of the sport. Educational courses are also run by:

Hampshire College of Agriculture,
Sparsholt,
Winchester,
Hants.

A RUNNER

EARLY MORNING

Henry Stannard.

FLYING LOW AND WARILY ALONG THE TOP OF THE HEATHER

1

GAMEKEEPING TODAY

Fig. 1.1 The Gamekeeper
(There are also female Gamekeepers)

Gamekeeping Today

Introduction

Historical and Modern

The gamekeeper's work today is both frustrating and demanding, physically and mentally. His life is made increasingly more difficult by the ever-changing facets of modern thinking. Earlier this century his sole role was protector of his employer's game. His three functions were the destruction of vermin, the rearing of game, and safeguarding against poachers. In the 1980s the gamekeeper needs to turn his hand to many more tasks. Where once a large staff was kept to assist with the supplementary chores such as rabbit control, maintenance of equipment, dogs, etc.., the burden now falls entirely on the keeper's shoulders.

His problems are diverse, but usually fall into one or two categories, i.e. modern agricultural techniques and the often misguided opinions of so-called animal or country lovers.

Few estates are owned and farmed by the gamekeeper's employer. A man who would be so much more aware of the interests of game and the relative influence any decisions he made would have on the future of his sport.

Possible conflict

The first problem many keepers are faced with is his relationship with the farm manager. So very many disagreements are caused by the simple inability of both to appreciate the other's point of view. A farm manager is employed to produce a profit and the gamekeeper is employed to produce game. Each has his own job to do and this must be taken into account. Disagreement usually begins over some trivial matter and grows beyond all sensible proportion. A conflict will develop between farm manager and keeper from what at first sight may seem a petty argument during the first few months. Unthinking farm managers may not realise that the hedge they intend to grub out may be a vital link to draw pheasants from a poor quality drive or dense woodland to a cover that will improve quality and produce results. A stubble left on the boundary may draw game away from the centre of the shoot and perhaps off it altogether. A farm manager may not even contemplate the many farming operations that may vex a keeper. Daily, there is something to cause discord, be it hedge cutting the day before a partridge shoot, machinery parked in gateways that game is to be driven through or past; stock turned into a field the day before a shoot, which knock down the gun pegs; combining at night where poults are known to be jukking; advisory staff tramping the fields inspecting crops or taking samples; routine tasks of straw burning and spraying. The latter is particularly a nuisance if herbicide is sprayed into hedge bottoms where game is nesting, destroying the cover and leaving nests open to predators.

To a keeper, the annoyances are limitless, but to the farm manager they are just part of the daily routine. From the alternative aspect, the keeper will gleefully count his wild stock in the evening as they appear on the freshly drilled corn to feast on the grain. He will consider it necessary to drive along the edge of some fields, as will the guns on a shoot day, and he views with satisfaction the weeds that appear among the game cover to add further attraction for game.

The work of gamekeeper and farm manager conflicts in so many ways that it is difficult to develop a mutual understanding. Yet they both work hard to harvest a crop that they have nurtured all year on the same estate.

Problems with outsiders

The other major problem that the keeper has to contend with is the 'nature lover' - the suburban do-gooder who wishes to turn the countryside into what he thinks it should be, instead of accepting it for what it naturally is.

The structure of the countryside has changed in the last few decades. In many areas, cottages that once housed farmworkers and keepers have been sold to commuters or week-enders. These incomers are often horrified when confronted by the ways of the countryside and immediately demand that alterations are made. They little realise that the estate that they found attractive enough to wish to buy a house and live on, is only preserved that way in the interests of field sports. These people move in, often into the best houses on the estate, and are of small value to the community. They offer little support to local shops, schools and transport, and yet expect to influence local matters.

The genuine conservationists have the welfare of the countryside at heart and are a much needed ally. They research the facts and do not let emotions cloud their judgment. So many 'nature lovers', however, share the belief that absolutely everything must be preserved. They would introduce an imbalance of nature where certain species would be allowed to multiply until they died of disease or starvation. Where those few species had so dominated the scene before their departure, a void would be left that could not be filled.

Many predators have adapted most readily to the pressures of modern life. It is for this reason that some control must be accepted as necessary, for without it, these species will eventually predominate over the species less able to adapt to life alongside man.

The role of the gamekeeper as vermin controller is unpopular with many who do not understand the necessity for such measures. This difficulty is increased by the fact that many species of vermin are extremely pretty. Foxes, squirrels, deer, jays and magpies are all attractive and are made welcome in many suburban gardens. Yet it is the keeper who is contacted when roe deer are eating the roses, foxes kill the chickens, magpies are devouring the song birds and squirrels invade the loft.

This illogical reasoning is carried even further by those condemning the keeper and his work. Every gamekeeper knows what a ruthless hunter the domestic cat can be, and yet so many of those who dislike the thought of birds and animals being deliberately killed condone this act by keeping one or more cats. Somewhere in their minds they find it acceptable to feed the song birds in their gardens and get them tame, while at the same time keeping the birds' worst enemy - a cat.

The majority of owners of working dogs, whether it be a gundog, a hound or a sheepdog, train and value their dogs and care for them in a responsible manner. Not always so with the ordinary pet owners who often allow their pets to roam loose, causing traffic accidents and generally being a nuisance to society.

Whenever a programme is shown on T.V. portraying one or another field sports, it arouses criticism and condemnation. Any wrong doing, which usually occurs by accident, immediately receives full coverage by the media. And yet day-after-day, programmes are shown and deeds reported of man's inhumanity to man, which provoke little or no reaction from the population.

This lack of reasoning so often confronts the keeper in his work and, being the type of man he is, makes it so difficult for him to understand.

Man's interference

Man's greed and interference has already caused an imbalance to nature, but it is only man's commonsense that will prevent it from worsening. In recent years, much research has been carried out to discover which environment is needed to promote an increase in wildlife. Plants, insects, animals, birds and fish have all been carefully studied. As a result, encouragement, both financial and advisory, is now available to improve the habitat.

Two prime examples of man's intervention during this century were the introduction of the grey squirrel and of the deadly disease in rabbits - myxamatosis. Both have had a devastating effect on the ecology of the British Isles.

The modern keeper

The average keeper needs to be a jack-of-all-trades; a manual worker who is sometimes involved in clerical work. He needs to be a diplomat, an organiser and a public relations officer. He has to be capable of giving commands and receiving them. He needs to be single minded in his cause and yet adaptable. The keeper needs basic knowledge in mechanical, electrical and veterinary matters. He needs to be able to estimate and calculate and to be resourceful enough to make the best out of what he has at his disposal. Sometimes he even needs to be a psychologist to deal with his employer, or others, when attempting to achieve his own way in order to get the best results.

The little used gift of common sense is the quality a keeper should most seek to develop. More often than not, it provides a simple answer to problems that arise.

Changing times

In Edwardian days at the beginning of this century, the head keeper of an estate occupied a privileged position on a par with the village doctor or school teacher. Nowadays, the keeper does not fit in socially anywhere. He is neither wanted by the public, nor by the farming community if they have no interest in shooting. Some of those who are interested in shooting genuinely care for the welfare of game, but there are many who shoot to either impress their friends or to satisfy their bloodlust.

Few young boys, sons of shooting men, are now sent with the gamekeeper to gain knowledge of his trade and the countryside. But many are presented with a gun and their introduction to game shooting is via the clay pigeon trap; soon after standing on a peg and having grouse, partridge or pheasant driven towards them. Appreciation and a full understanding of the work involved are never learned, nor its value to wildlife and the countryside in general.

Research shows the importance of predator control for the well-being of game, and conditions that suit game also suit many other species. Yet now, in many cases an extra hundred or two pheasants are reared to compensate for lack of vermin control, a situation that is worsened because so many part-time keepers are employed where once they were all full-time.

Employers so often see no monetary gain in employing a full time keeper to kill vermin for several months of the year when a part-time man can be employed for six months to look after poults and to organise a few shoots. In the long run this will prove detrimental to the ecology, but the progress is slow and results are judged from year to year, not from one generation to another.

Shoot Day standards

Pride, respect and etiquette are old fashioned words in today's vocabulary. Future generations will probably not even know what they mean. They are all qualities that should be developed, understood and appreciated by all concerned with field sports.

The keeper should be well-mannered and well-dressed on a shoot day. He should wear the suit of clothes provided for the purpose, complete with a tie and a hat. He may need to be firm, but never rude.

The guns who shoot should respect their quarry and be fully aware and appreciative of the work involved to produce it. Good manners should predominate. Greedy and dangerous shooting should not be condoned. The recent upsurge of letting shooting by the day has, in some cases, lowered the standard of etiquette. When money has been paid, the selfish gun will take the attitude that he intends to get his money's worth. He can see no credit in leaving a poor flying bird, for it will not benefit him if it flies better later in the season. Shooting is made available to everyone and many individuals neither know nor care much about the sport they have spent money to become involved in.

It is disheartening for a keeper who has worked hard all year to see his birds shot at with as much respect as a clay pigeon would receive. Small wonder that so many become disillusioned and end up caring less about pride in the work and more about the financial gain to be had from it.

The Gamekeeper is an asset

There is a place in modern times for a gamekeeper providing he can accept and be accepted. The conservationist would do well to work with, instead of against, the keeper as each has much to offer to the other. The keeper's knowledge is gained from practical experience not just from books, or university degrees. The new discoveries that the naturalist thinks he has made are often already well known to the keeper who has learned from a previous generation. So many times he can predict what will happen without ever fully knowing the reasons why. The keeper sees different things as they occur each day, his ability to observe is often a measure of his success. He accepts it is the nature of each creature to behave in a certain way - his judgment is not influenced by emotion or the beauty of any particular animal. The blunt facts of life and death surround him at all times and he accepts them.

The gamekeeper should be valued as an asset to an estate. His vigilance over his game extends over the whole estate and property is also safeguarded by a keeper on his rounds. At night time it is the keeper who checks out strange cars and, during the day, it is he who requests that dogs are kept on leads, that rubbish is taken home and gates kept shut. The keeper is on call night and day when anything is amiss.

Large numbers

Many voices are raised against the shooting of big bags of game. Criticism is often levelled at the keeper, but he is working to instructions and it is his job to provide his employer with what he wants or he may be dismissed. In many cases greed and unsporting behaviour is provoked by the lack of birds, not too many. The critics should judge whether it is more acceptable to shoot a thousand birds in a day and to then rest a beat for three weeks than it is to shoot four or five times on that beat during the same period and average two hundred a day.

The word 'slaughter' is frequently used when describing a large daily bag, and yet if slaughter is taken to mean shooting inferior quality or birds at close range, this much more frequently happens on small days. A plentiful supply of pheasants driven over the guns allows for the selection of quality.

A day's shooting should be judged by the atmosphere and etiquette that prevails, not by the number of birds shot, be it many or few.

The local hunt

Gamekeepers do not generally get on well with the hunting fraternity, even though in some cases the employer is also a hunting man. Keepers know only too well what damage a litter of foxes can cause to game. The continued discovery, day after day, of sitting pheasants or partridges pulled off nests and the eggs eaten; and the horrific discovery of literally hundreds of pheasant poults killed in or around a release pen, are clear reasons why the fox cannot be tolerated on a shoot, during the spring and summer.

However, the field sports fraternity have got to present a united front or they will not exist at all. It will cause no significant harm for a fox to be present on a shoot at the end of the season, when the hunt may be invited, if it will keep all parties happy. If the keeper obliges in such a way, then the hunt, too, should oblige and feep off feed rides and make every effort possible to kill the fox.

The hunting fraternity hastily take advantage of any chance to shift publicity from themselves to elsewhere. They publicly announce that their methods are the only humane way of controlling the fox population and that it is beyond reproach compared with the keeper's use of gun or snare. Gamekeepers know the true position. Resentment builds up when such criticism is levelled openly.

The opinion is sometimes formed that the hunting brigade are arrogant and have little regard for any sport other than their own. This may not be true, but the feeling does exist.

Many shoots have to pay thousands of pounds for the lease of a shoot, but the hunt pays nothing for the use of the land, nor will it compensate for losses to game caused by a resident fox population.

At all times field sports must support each other, and every sportsman should belong to one organisation or another that contributes towards research, representation in parliament and the promotion of his chosen sport. Without this allegiance, there will be no future for shooting or any other field sport. Those who hunt must work with those who shoot in a way which maximises benefit for both sides and both sides must do nothing to attract unwelcome publicity to the other's sport.

Gamekeeping work available

Gamekeeping requires dedication, honesty, tactfulness and the liking of one's own company.

Situations are usually advertised in the press between January and May. More often than not, the availability of jobs is passed by word of mouth and vacancies are filled before the advertisement appears. The keepers' grapevine is well supported and information is passed throughout the country quickly.

A shoot may be run under varying conditions. Sometimes the landowner organises the shoot, sometimes the tenant farmer or sometimes the shooting rights are leased off as a separate enterprise to the farms. The shoot may be financed by a private individual, a syndicate who share the annual cost, or by shooting let by the day. Various combinations may be involved to meet expenses.

On some estates the head keeper is left solely in charge. The policy will have been previously arranged with his employer, but the day-to-day organisation and minor financial matters will be put in his hands. It is his responsibility to run the shoot efficiently with as little bother to his employer as possible.

In other cases the shoot owner prefers to take a more active part in the running of the shoot and will expect the keeper to be available at any time to discuss arrangements and to inspect the estate.

Some shoots are run on a commercial scale, with many birds being reared at the expense of good keepering.

Other shoots are managed more traditionally and time spent on vermin control, nesting, etc., is regarded as valuable and not a waste of money.

The generation of keepers that has recently retired, were trained in this latter method. They started off as keepers' boys and were even expected to dig the head keeper's garden, as well as wash out the kennels and creosote the coops. They started at the bottom to learn their profession and, as they attained the position of head keeper, they expected the respect and deference shown to them that they, in turn, had shown to their head keeper.

Times have changed, and there is no room for such luxury. Most head keepers now have to work and pull their weight alongside the under- or beat-keepers.

Conditions of the job

Positions that are advertised should be investigated fully. Obviously, the house offered will be viewed, wages discussed and the shoot looked at. But deeper influences will affect the keeper's ability to do a good job. Farming policies, possibility of poaching, proximity of other shoots and the relationship with the local hunt are but a few of the factors that will affect results.

Originally, keepers' houses stood on their own, often somewhat isolated. But now many have been sold off and the keeper is expected to live in an ordinary farm cottage which is often semi- detached. This can be a problem if the keeper's dogs bark and upset the neighbours, or a nosey and untrustworthy person lives nearby who makes himself familiar with the keeper's whereabouts and routine.

The original keepers' houses always had kennels and outhouses available for his use, but now these are often lacking.

Wages offered are usually slightly higher than the agricultural rate, but no overtime is paid which can mean that frequently the keeper is financially worse off than the farm worker. It is for this reason that tips are gratefully received and a bonus for results appreciated. Keepers are expected to be on call day and night, every single week. Many extra hours are put in during the rearing season, weekends and on night patrol, for which there is no payment.

To compensate for the low wage, numerous 'perks' may be offered which, if accounted for in monetary value, would add a further 30 or 40 percent to the wage.

The house is usually offered rent and rates free. Maintenance is paid for outside and often paint is supplied free of charge for internal decorating. A telephone is usually supplied free, or at a reduced charge.

Electricity may be paid for. A vehicle is often provided free of charge for work. A suit of clothes or water proof clothing is provided annually. Food is often provided for two dogs and cartridges for vermin control. Milk, potatoes, firewood, etc. may all be provided where available.

Employers usually accept that the responsible keeper takes time off when it is available. A keeper is sometimes criticised for taking time off during a week day, without it being taken into account that he is out most evenings until it gets dark and frequently after it is dark. He will also have routine work to attend to at weekends and be at the beck and call of his employer. Holidays are usually taken at a time that fits in with the work, often a bone of contention within the family. If a Boxing Day shoot is organised, not only does the keeper have to work that day, but Christmas Day as well to prepare for the shoot. The keeper needs an understanding wife, not only at this time, but at others when she has to answer the 'phone, run errands or is dragged outside to shut up poults on a wet night, to wash eggs or to feed the dogs.

STARTING A NEW JOB

When a keeper starts a new job there are several things he should do:

1. Procure a map of the shoot and familiarise himself with the ground and the boundaries. He should locate public footpaths, bridle ways, etc.

2. Ask to be introduced to tenant farmers and other property owners on the estate.

3. Carefully plan snare and trap lines to fit in with the feeding routine to save time.

4. Introduce himself to neighbouring keepers; their help may be needed one day.

SUMMARY

The keeper's life style has a certain charisma about it. A romantic image that attracts the envy of many. The idyllic vision of the tweed suit, the gun under one arm, a faithful spaniel at heel and a preaceful countryside is a far cry from reality.

Indeed, there are odd times when the image is fulfilled, and the pleasure is great at such a time. It is these rare moments that make the work worthwhile and which provides the motivation to face reality.

More often than not, though, a keeper's life is one of drudgery and worry. So many of the problems that face him are beyond his control. The weather, the attitude of people and the uncertainty of dealing with living creatures are all causes of deep concern. Yet these and other things provide the challenge that keepers enjoy. Every keeper moans about his way of life, but there are few who would exchange it for any other career.

JUST GOING TO ROOST

2

The Pheasant keeper's year
including organising a shoot day

2.1 To keep freshly shot game in good condition it must be hung, well spaced, in a cool place and protected from flies. The game dealer should be notified as soon as possible and collection arranged.. The cash return to the shoot is as little as one tenth the cost of production.

(Picture courtesy Hardwick Game Farm, Suffolk)

The Pheasant Keeper's Year

The Pheasant (Phasianus colchicus)
Shooting Season 1 Oct - 1 Feb inclusive

Pheasants

Range covers the whole of Great Britain. The pheasanrt is reared in large quantities for shooting and also breed in the wild, thriving best on well drained land where predators are kept at a minimum. Many different strains exist, the common coloured being divided into ring necks, black necks, mongolian and the lighter coloured Chinese. These have been so interbred that few examples of the pure strains now exist. The black type are known as *Melanistics* and include the Japanese Green. A lighter sandy-coloured type is known as a *Bohemian* and a partially or pure white type is sometimes seen.

Wild pheasants lay up to 15 eggs in an open nest on the ground. The incubation period is 24 days. The cocks are polygamous and do not help to rear the young. The hens are not generally good mothers. The chicks feed on insect life for the first few days. Pheasants in captivity will lay about 30 eggs, from which a hatch of 60-70% should be achieved. The young are normally artificially reared until at least six weeks old, when they are released into open-topped release pens built in woodland.

2.2 Cock Pheasants are polygamous, but do not help to rear their young.

Woodcock (Scolopax Rusticola)
Shooting Season 1 Oct - 31 Jan
(England and Wales)
1 Sept - 31 Jan (Scotland)

Woodcock are present throughout the year, but numbers are increased by winter visitors. They pair up and the male marks his territory by flying slowly back and forth and calling a combination of frog-like croaks and a whistling noise. This display is known as 'roding'. Two broods are reared between March and June. The 4 eggs are laid in a nest on the ground. The hen only sits, but the young are tended by both parents. Woodcock feed mainly on worms, insects, etc. They are reputed to 'airlift' their young to safety by carrying them between the thighs when disturbed. Woodcock are included in the ban on shooting wildfowl and waders imposed during a period of hard weather.

A Monthly Account
February and March

February is a month when the majority of keepers who wish to move, change jobs. At the end of the shooting season vacancies are advertised and the situations vacant columns are scoured for a position that offers better opportunities. In days past, there were sufficient vacancies for keepers to select from, but in present times there are scores of applicants for every job that becomes available.

The first chores of a new season are to catch up the stock required for breeding and to continue feeding. Vermin control will begin in earnest and rabbiting will be carried out before the undergrowth begins to grow and the rabbits start to breed. The keeper's attention may also need to be turned to pigeon control on rape or newly drilled corn. Rats, too, should be dealt with while still hungry and living around farm buildings and stacks.

Release pens should be repaired or constructed while there is little cover in the woods. If attended to early in the year, the vegetation will have a chance to become re-established well before the pen is needed.

Spring is frequently the only time of the year that a keeper has a chance to take a holiday, if he is committed to rearing his own birds.

2.3 Woodcock often arrive at the onset of hard weather and several may be accounted for in a day's shooting

April

In April the breeding stock will begin to lay and birds in the wild to nest. Hatching equipment must be prepared. The hedgerows and woods will be searched for nests and a watch kept on them. Vermin control will be stepped up as the breeding season increases activity and general movement. At the end of the month a start will be made on preparing the rearing equipment. The incubators will become filled as the breeding stock penned continue to come into lay.

May

May is a busy month; wild game birds' nests will continue to be monitored. Frequently pheasants will share a nest with each other or French partridge and some of the eggs may need to be removed. The penned stock will be in full lay, the incubators will be filled, and the first hatch taken off. The equipment on the rearing field should be erected and the grass trimmed if necessary. As the month goes on the work increases with subsequent hatches. Deserted nests in the wild will be picked up and a few broody hens or bantams may be used to take care of these, making yet another daily chore. All the time, vermin control will continue and any rookeries on the estate may require extra attention as the young begin to leave the nest. Foxes that have not been dealt with will be moving their cubs about and a constant watch must be kept against any taking up residence on the shoot.

The keeper will have to spare time to make sure that proposed game crops are planted and attended to in time to provide the necessary cover on shoot days.

June

By June, vermin control will be forcibly curtailed by the combination of the height and density of agricultural crops and the pressure of work on the rearing field. Hatching will continue although no more eggs may be set after the middle of the month. As the numbers on the rearing field increase, debeaking and bitting will become routine chores. Care must be taken to identify any disease immediately it becomes apparent and deal with it accordingly. Young chicks will need to be driven into the brooder huts at night and older ones too, if the weather is bad. Breeding stock will be released either into standing crops or preferably into release pens. Brails and spex, if used, must be removed.

June and July are hectic months for keepers. So many things require attention that there is little spare time. The daylight hours are long and the work seems endless.

2.4 Natural food will entice pheasants away from the feed ride. Acorns are a favourite, as are the discs (sometimes called spangles) on the back of oak leaves

2.5 Reared pheasants are less successful in raising young in the wild than truly wild birds

July

During July the first hatched poults will be ready to go to the woods. The final preparations will be made to release pens before the poults are crated and released inside. The later hatched chicks will be growing and any partridges reared will remain on the field until the harvest is well underway.

August

August will see the beginning of the harvest and the keeper may need to spend time where the combines are working if there is the possibility of a fox laying in the corn.

Pheasant poults will continue to be released and, as the rearing pens become empty, they can be dismantled, disinfected and stored away. Small pens can be erected where stubble and straw have been cleared or burned for the release of partridges.

Feed rides in release pens can be strawed up and the poults will continue to be fed at least twice a day. As the corn is cut, the estate will become opened up and the keeper will spend time driving around to see how the wild game stock has fared. The older poults may have flown out of the release pens and have started to wander and the keeper may have to regularly drive in to prevent them straying off the estate.

September

By September most of the partridges should be released and plans will already be made for the coming shoot days. Stubbles, insects and natural plant food such as blackberries, beech nuts and acorns will tempt the adventurous pheasant poults to stray. The keeper will observe the most likely places for leakage off the shoot and continually drive in where possible. Towards the end of the month a few outlying covers will be fed and a routine developed so that feeding is established wherever pheasants are required to be located for a shoot day.

Duck flighting will probably begin on ponds that are visited by duck and, as the natural food decreases, feeding will need to be increased.

October

October is the month when officially pheasant shooting begins, although most often pheasants are not touched until the end of the month. To begin with Partridge drives may be arranged and later in the month a few pheasants may be included.

The leaf canopy in the woods will still be thick, so pheasant shooting will be concentrated on hedgerows and game cover. Most keepers continue to feed their release pens twice daily, even though the poults will have spread to other areas. A watch must now be kept against poachers, particularly those shooting from car windows. Pheasants should be discouraged from roosting near to public roads and the keeper should make sure that he can be seen patrolling the roads at roosting time.

Plans will be made for the main pheasant shoots to come and extra pickers up and beaters may need to be organised. Gun stands in woodlands may need to be cut, sewelling renewed and gun pegs cut and placed in position. Beater's tracks may also need to be cut, stiles made or bags tied on fences that need to be crossed.

November

November is the month when the pheasant shooting begins in earnest. The leaf will be coming off, making the woods lighter and it easier for the birds to fly. A neighbouring keeper may want a beater or picker up and if he provides help on a shoot day, then the favour should be returned. Regular feeding will continue and an even greater watch kept for poachers. The pressure is on the keeper as he awaits to discover the results of his previous nine months' work. An odd woodcock may appear in the bag, perhaps an indication of hard weather to come.

December

December continues much the same as November, but will fall into some kind of routine. The days are very short and, although the release pen sites will probably only be fed once a day after they have been shot for the first time, the other feeding will still need to be done daily. If the keeper cannot get around on the day he shoots, or he attends some other shoot, it may be necessary to feed some places the evening or night before. Feeding should not be neglected.

Many employers arrange to shoot on Boxing Day. Sometimes these are less formal occasions involving family and friends. If a full day's shooting is planned, the keeper will have to work most of Christmas Day to make the necessary preparations.

January

In January the pressure will have eased off as the bulk of the shooting will probably be over. On some shoots, **cocks only** will be the order, but on others, cocks and hens will continue to be shot until the end of the season. A start may be made on **catching up**.

At the end of the month the keeper may be allowed to arrange his own cock shoot. It is a chance he has of saying a thank you to beaters and pickers-up who have assisted him through the season and of seeing old friends. Sometimes another day is arranged for tenant farmers, managers and other associates to shoot.

End of Season

Occasionally an end of season dinner is provided by the keepers' employers and this is much appreciated by those present. The last week of January is usually a busy time socially for keepers, who may get invited to several cock shoots. Often it is the only opportunity during the year to renew old acquaintances. An end- of-term atmosphere prevails and there is always great discussion as to who is moving where, and what jobs may become available.

February

Then, suddenly, it is February and it is all finished. The dog is left in the kennel, its services probably not required until the late summer. The pheasants become settled on the feed rides and the cocks appear in the fields. Already the nettles in the woods are beginning to show signs of growth and another year has begun.

2.6 The original game cart. The modern equivalent is a trailer pulled by a 4-wheel-drive vehicle.

Organising a Shoot Day
(see also 'Presenting Quality Birds', Chapter 7)

Shoot days are the culmination of the year's work. A keeper is judged by his results; therefore, much is at stake. Many keepers suffer sleepless nights both before and after shoot days, as they worry about the forthcoming day or analyse the one just gone. Close liaison with the employer and careful planning are necessary to ensure a satisfactory day.

Achieving the number

On days that are let, the visiting guns will be expecting a certain number of birds. These days are particularly difficult to arrange, for the keeper may not know how well the guns can shoot or how selective they may be. It is as well, therefore, to have alternative plans should it become apparent that the required total will either not be achieved or is likely to be exceeded. This can be done by having two or three *alternative* drives available where more or less birds are likely to be shown.

Syndicate days can also be difficult to arrange. Some members may only be subscribing to half a gun, therefore it is necessary to balance the days to give all members a fair share throughout the season.

Private shoot owners vary in their expectations. Some prefer even days *throughout* the season, while others may prefer to have a *few* larger days.

2.7 A feed "steddle". Straw is used both on the roof and on the ground to provide a dry area for pheasants to feed and scratch

The traditional way of shooting is the easiest to organise. The pheasant season would begin in late October and continue through November with the outside covers being shot. The main covers would be shot in late November and December to provide the bigger days, while January would be spent where the birds had settled. Often cocks only would be the order of the day towards the end of the season.

Planning a Shoot Day

Planning a shoot day will begin well in advance. Covers that are likely to be shot will be concentrated on. Feeding will be planned to encourage the birds to be there at the required time of day.

Game crops are best shot in the morning or early afternoon. Later in the day pheasants will be returning to the woods to roost.

A well laid out estate may provide large days. The morning drives may be driven towards central covers which can be shot in the afternoon, thus the birds may be shown at least twice in the same day. When even days are required, covers and game crops surrounding release sites may be shot several times before the actual release site is driven.

Psychologically, it is as well to arrange to have good drives first in the morning, immediately prior to the lunch break, and then last of the day. These are the drives that guns are most likely to remember.

Effect of the weather

The weather can play a large part in determining the success or failure of the day. Contrary to the opinion held by many guns, a frosty morning followed by bright sunshine is not the ideal weather. This rarely proves to be unless a change in the weather is imminent. Sunshine often results in pheasants being reluctant to fly well. **The ideal weather for showing and handling birds is a dull, damp day with a light wind.** A fresh fall of snow will make pheasants difficult to handle. Shoot days should be cancelled if there is deep snow, torrential rain or thick fog.

Oddly enough, pheasants will also come onto the feed rides much better on dull, damp days than they will in bright sunshine. They are mysterious creatures and many a keeper has worried for days over the disappearance of his birds, only to have them reappear on feed rides and feed as though they had never been gone.

Generally, pheasants are not fed on the day they are shot. Other beats should be fed on the night before or early in the morning of a shoot day so that food is available for them as usual.

Engaging Beaters and Pickers-up

Beaters and pickers-up must be booked as soon as possible and regulars will soon learn their way around. Only keen or experienced and honest people should be employed as shoot days offer guided tours of the estate which the dishonest will soon take advantage of. One bad beater can disrupt the whole beating line; many birds may escape back through a gap left in the line; therefore, he or she must not be tolerated. A reliable beater who comes regularly is invaluable to a keeper.

Beaters should not be allowed to bring a dog if it is not under control at all times. Even good steady dogs will turn birds back over the beaters if the wind is blowing from behind them. Dogs will work forward before winding the scent and turning back towards the bird. Nonetheless, dogs are very useful in thick cover, although it is inevitable that they will catch a few birds. When there is little cover or the beaters are close together, having gathered the pheasants into the heading of the drive, then dogs should be kept at heel. The keeper must be in full control of his team of beaters.

Reliable members of the team should be informed of the day's plans and any particular chores they may be asked to perform.

Where one or more under-keepers are employed, it is important that they should be familiar with the day's plans. Transport must be arranged for beaters, pickers-up and dead game as well as the guns. Money will be needed to be drawn to pay the beaters and pickers-up.

Placing the guns

Gun pegs should be placed at a reasonable distance from the drive at the estimated place a pheasant will achieve optimum height, and approximately 35 yards apart. Guns are most often placed in a semi-circle for pheasant shooting, while a straight line is preferable for partridges. Some pheasant drives may need a walking gun, who will accompany the beaters, to deal with birds that break out of the sides or turn back.

Guns in most areas are numbered from the right as they face the drive. Where space is limited, it may be necessary to double bank the guns, but this should be avoided if possible.

Driving pheasants

The keeper must endeavour to provide all the guns with a share of the shooting. Allowance must be made for the strength and direction of the wind. By watching which way the birds are facing, the keeper can judge in which direction they are likely to fly and adjust the beating line accordingly.

The Shoot Day

The keeper should arrive punctually at the shoot meet. He should wear the suit provided, complete with a tie and a hat. He should confirm that the shoot organiser is familiar with the day's plans.

At the end of the day, a brace of pheasants or other game should be selected and given to each shooting guest. Guns, if requested, should be thoroughly cleaned. The rest of the dead game should be hung in a safe place with ample space for it to cool quickly.

Shoot days should be enjoyed by everyone concerned, but a happy atmosphere will only prevail if there has been a lot of careful planning and thought beforehand.

2.8 Cock Pheasant

(Courtesy: Mr. C. Knight)

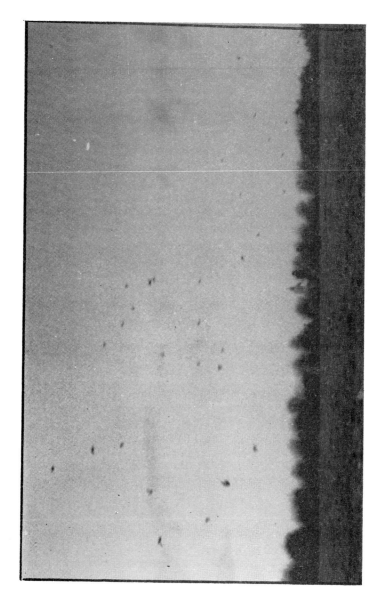

2.9 Pheasants flushed from Game cover

3
Vermin Control and Hazards to Game

Recommended Reading
Game Conservancy Advisory Numbers 7, 16 and 22
also Predatory Mammals in Britain

SPECIES INCLUDED
Winged Vermin
Crow (Carrion and Hooded)
Coot and Moorhen
Jackdaw
Jay
Magpie
Rook
Starling
Pigeon

Species that are protected by law
Tawny Owl
Buzzard
Harrier
Sparrowhawk

Carrion Crow

Jackdaw

Jay

Magpie

Rook

Starling

3.1 Various Winged Vermin

Mammalian Vermin
Cat
Coypu
Fox
Hedgehog
Mink
Rabbit
Rat
Squirrel
Stoat
Weasel

Other Species included
Deer
Dog
Hare
Mole

Species protected by law
Badger

Predator Control and the Law*

The destruction of vermin is closely controlled by law; there is tight legislation concerning methods of control and species that may be destroyed.

The use of gin traps, self-locking snares and poisons, (other than for rodents), unless a special licence has been granted, are all now illegal.

All species of hawks and owls are protected and heavy fines may be imposed. The *Wildlife and Countryside Act* (1981) listed species of birds into different categories; some being given greater protection than others. The Act is divided into three schedules :

Schedule I under which the listed species are protected by special penalties;

Schedule 2, Part I species with open seasons during which period they may be killed;

* See separate Chapter on the legal aspects

3.2 Sparrow Hawk feeding young. All species of hawks, falcons and owls are protected by law.

Courtesy: Mr. C. Knights

and Schedule 2, Part II which consists of species that are classed as pests and may be killed at any time.

So far as the gamekeeper is concerned, many of the birds included in Schedule I can cause harm, particularly to wild stock. A few, such as sparrow hawks, tawny owl, little owl, kestrel and common buzzard, might possibly be taken if it could be proved in a court of law that they were killed to prevent serious damage to livestock. Pheasants and partridges are normally only regarded as livestock when fully contained in a pen. Wild stocks would not be included within this exception, so keepers are very limited in their powers to kill birds of prey.

Animal predators are a different matter, and only three are fully protected, i.e., wild cat, pine marten, and the otter. A second category which includes the polecat and hedgehog give the animals protection from certain methods of control such as poison, gas, traps, snares and night shooting. This appears to leave shooting during daylight hours as the only method of control. These restrictions, especially when imposed on such a common and harmful animal as the hedgehog, seem somewhat unnecessary and difficult to implement. It is virtually impossible to prevent a hedgehog entering a tunnel trap set for a rat or stoat.

Badgers are also now protected and may only be killed when deemed necessary by the Ministry of Agriculture, who will then grant a special licence. Red squirrels are fully protected.

Effects of Predators

The control of vermin is of variable importance, depending on the area, type of shoot and rearing policies. Every keeper should do all he can to control the number of predators. Where wild birds contribute a high proportion to the bag, then control must be extended throughout the year. In other areas where wild birds do not naturally thrive and the policy is to rear considerable numbers, and to shoot hard and leave very little stock, vermin control should receive priority in the spring from February to May. After this, rearing and releasing will have to come first, although control should be resumed during August and September. During the summer, trapping is often made difficult by tall and thick vegetation and growing corn. It is also a time of less movement by predators when family groups are still together.

Winged vermin is particularly harmful to game - crows and magpies (which have greatly increased in recent years) being the worst. Protected birds of prey normally only cause damage to chicks and poults, but members of the crow family take eggs as well and it is at the laying period that most of the harm is done. Eggs that have had holes made in them and the contents

3.3 The Fox is the gamekeeper's worst enemy

sucked out will identify the work of a bird. Carcasses with many of the bones left intact, but cleaned of flesh, will also provide a clue to an avian predator.

Knowledge and detective work can often indicate which predator has made a kill. Signs of fresh droppings, fur or feather, and footprints in soft mud will all provide clues to the presence of vermin and identification of species. Small woodland birds such as blackbirds will mob a predator in their midst and their alarm calls should not go unheeded.

Large mammals such as foxes, mink and feral cats can cause damage throughout the year and should be dealt with whenever possible. Smaller mammals and winged vermin are most harmful during the breeding season. It is illegal to poison, snare or spring trap birds, so control is limited to the use of a gun or a cage trap. A lamp at night must not be used when shooting birds.

The trapping network should be carefully planned to be efficient. A route should be considered that will include as large an area as possible of worthwhile sites. A circular route can take in much more ground than walking back over the same track and can be covered in much the same time. Likewise, traps set near feeding places can be checked at the same time.

Summary of the methods available for vermin control

SHOOTING A small bore rifle or a shotgun may be used, providing they are not fully automatic weapons. A lamp must not be used at night for shooting winged vermin. These restrictions do not apply to animals that are **NOT** included in Schedules 5 or 6; i.e. rabbits, rats, etc.

POISONS The only poisons freely available are for rats and mice. **Warfarin** can also be used for the control of grey squirrels. This must be contained in a specially designed hopper so that other species cannot reach it. Its use is only permitted in certain districts.

At all times, poisons used for rodent control must not provide a hazard for other livestock. It should either be placed well down holes, under cover or in hoppers. Pre-mixed poison is available as a meal, in granular form on cut wheat, in blocks, or packeted in sachets for ease of distribution. It is also manufactured as a concentrate when it can be mixed with meal or whole grain. The addition of sugar in the bait mixed for rats is sometimes recommended and bird seed, as used for canaries, provides a good base for a mouse bait. Sachets and blocks may be dragged from beneath cover.

Whichever form is chosen, **it must be administered every day** until such time **as it ceases to go.**

Feral cats are ruthless hunters. Cage trapping is recommended.

3.4 Other predators of Game or nuisances

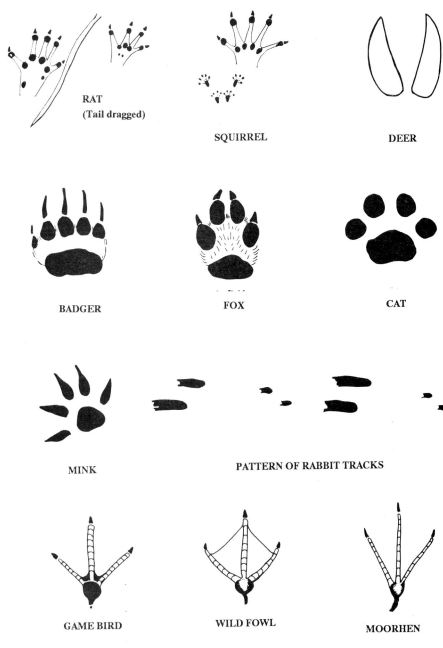

RAT
(Tail dragged)

SQUIRREL

DEER

BADGER

FOX

CAT

MINK

PATTERN OF RABBIT TRACKS

GAME BIRD

WILD FOWL

MOORHEN

3.5 IDENTIFICATION OF TRACKS

It is useless to poison for a day or two, have a break, and then resume poisoning. This not only gives the rodents a chance to recover from the first dose, but may also make them shy of taking future bait and build up a resistance to the poison. Therefore, it is imperative that baiting must continue until there is no longer any signs of life.

Two other poisons are available for specified uses only, under licence from the Ministry of Agriculture.

1. **ALPHACHLORALOSE** is available for the control of feral pigeons and mice.

2. **STRYCHNINE** is available for control of moles. This is administered by coating earth worms with the poison and placing them in mole runs well beneath the ground.

GASSING is restricted to animals living underground; namely foxes, rabbits, moles and rats.

Two chemicals are available for this purpose and must be handled with great care. Safety precautions must be taken during use. It should be stored in a tightly sealed container in a well ventilated place under lock and key. The chemical should be handled carefully to avoid inhaling or swallowing. It should not be used in wet or windy weather or in confined spaces. Children and livestock must be kept away from the vicinity during gassing operations, and contamination of streams and ponds avoided.

HYDROGEN CYANIDE is more familiarly known as **CYMAG** It is a white powder that quickly reacts with the air and moisture. A hand- operated pump or a long handled spoon should be used to place it well down in the holes. These should be immediately sealed with bags, earth or turves. The holes should not be re- opened for at least twenty-four hours and even then, great caution will be needed as the gas will still be strong.

Hydrogen Cyanide is a quick-acting poison and the fumes, if accidentally inhaled, can quickly cause unconsciousness. It is advisable to work with an assistant if at all possible and to have some capsules of amyl nitrite at hand, which acts as an antedote, in case of emergency. Empty tins should be filled with earth and buried.

3.6 Badger setts on the side of an open bank

3.7 The Badger now protected by law

ALUMINIUM PHOSPHIDE is marketed as **PHOSTOXIN** and is for use in controlling rabbits, rats and moles. It is manufactured in tablet form which is convenient to use when dealing with these smaller animals.

SNARES are primarily used for catching foxes and rabbits. It is illegal to use them to catch deer, badgers or birds.

By law, snares must be inspected at least once a day, preferably in the mornings. Self-locking snares are now banned.

All snares must be securely anchored. Light weight rabbit snares are not suitable to use to catch foxes, for which much stronger wire is needed. A swivel and a stop should be incorporated into a fox wire; the stop is designed to prevent deer and such like being caught around the leg. A wooden peg or tealer is used to support the snare at the correct height; a slit is made across the top in which the wire is wedged. A general guidance to size and height from the ground is that the snare will be the same size as a man's head and the width of his hand above the ground. Care must be taken to select a site where no domestic pets or farm livestock are likely to be caught. Deer runs should also be avoided and, in areas where deer abound, it is suggested that a stick is laid or bent above the snare to encourage them to jump over.

Needless to say, it is unwise to set snares beside public roads, footpaths or bridleways.

It is not only false economy, but cruel as well, to use wire that is not strong enough to hold a fox. Much suffering is caused if the wire is broken and remains deeply embedded in the flesh of the escaped creature.

A few snares set in well chosen places will yield better results than many set without previous thought and observation. They are there ready and waiting for twenty-four hours a day, providing they are properly tended.

Not all areas are suitable for snaring, particularly where sheep and cattle roam free. A large population of hares also make snaring impractical, but these often seem to coincide with a low population of foxes. Trimming back of vegetation in the runs will be necessary during the summer to prevent snares becoming grown in.

Rabbit snares should be set where there are signs of activity. Well defined 'runs' will be obvious where the cover is short; it is on these that the snares are set. They must be securely pegged down and visited at least once a day, preferably in the early morning.

TRAPPING There are three different methods of trapping: Spring traps, Cage traps and Box traps.

It is illegal to set spring traps to catch birds.

3.8 Fox snares must be securely fastened and inspected at least once each day

3.9 Gin traps are now illegal

Spring Traps

There are several different designs of spring traps, all of which crush the victim. The most commonly used are the **Fenn Mk. IV** for small animals, and the Mk. VI for larger animals such as rabbits.

These types of traps must always be set under cover, whether by building tunnels in which to place them, or by using drains, hollow trees, etc. The larger traps used for rabbits must be placed well within the holes.

Tunnels can be built from any available material. Three 6 inch boards can be nailed together to form the basic shape. The tunnel should be at least 18 inches long and of sufficient width and height to accommodate the trap in both the set and sprung positions. The entrances at both ends should be guarded by either strong sticks or stones, etc., to prevent access by larger animals and birds. The dry soil inside the tunnel is very attractive to birds looking for somewhere to dust. The entrance area should also be kept clear of vegetation and vermin can be guided into the tunnel by digging or clearing a run in.

There is controversy among keepers as to whether the trap inside should be covered with fine soil. It should definitely be set in the ground so that the plate is level and it is generally considered best to cover it lightly. There is also the added bonus that it will be less obvious to prying human eyes.

The trap should be set as lightly as possible with the safety catch in place. This must be removed when the trap has been satisfactorily placed. A stout peg should be hammered into the ground to prevent the trap from being moved.

The siting of tunnels should be carefully considered and should avoid being near public areas. Obvious runs may be found along ditches, fences, banks, walls and hedgerows. Gateways, too, often prove a good position. Tunnels can be dug through banks and existing drains utilised, as can hollow trees.

Tunnel traps are not usually baited, but sometimes rabbit guts or the urine of stoat or weasel are used to provide an interesting odour.

Before new traps are used, they should be buried in the ground to rid them of their shine and smell. This is also recommended before use for old traps that have been oiled and stored. **The use of gin traps is now illegal.**

Box Traps

These are wooden tunnels of sizes that are suited to what they are required to catch. One end is open and the other covered with wire mesh. The trap

Stoat caught in a Fenn trap inside well camouflaged tunnel

3.10 Fenn Mk IV are the most commonly used trap.

Here shown in the set position. Note the safety catch is off, the plate is lightly set on the tongue and the plate is neither raised in the air nor so low that there is no room for leverage.

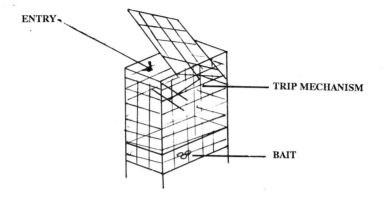

ENTRY

TRIP MECHANISM

BAIT

This type of trap was once used to catch hawks. This is now illegal but it can still be used for trapping magpies, etc.

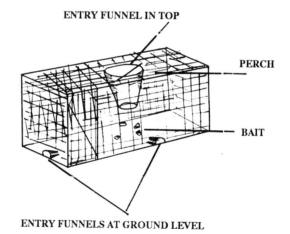

ENTRY FUNNEL IN TOP

PERCH

BAIT

ENTRY FUNNELS AT GROUND LEVEL

LARGE SECTIONAL CAGE TRAP

3.11 DIAGRAM OF CAGE TRAPS FOR BIRDS

3.12 Traps are often set on rafts and baited with carrots or sugar beet to catch coypu

3.13 Tunnel constructed from dead wood. Note sticks restricting size of entrance

acts on a see-saw principle. The creature enters the open end and tips the see-saw back so that it locks the creature in. This is unharmed and should be removed and humanely killed. Often box traps are set in pairs to face in opposite directions and similar sites are selected as would be used for tunnel traps.

Cage Traps

Cage traps are designed for many different purposes, from catching winged vermin to mammals of any size. Some are 'multi- catch' with a holding compartment, and others are 'single catch'.

Cage Traps designed for Winged Vermin

These are usually constructed from wire netting and preferably in sections. Entry is either via a funnel or short entrance in the top of the cage, or by tunnel at ground level. The disadvantage with the latter design is that sometimes game is caught.

The traps should be set up in feeding areas or on known flight lines and will probably need moving after a successful catch. They should be in the shade, contain food and water, and should be visited once a day at least, when set.

To be successful, the cage should be left wide open and baited inside and out for a few days. When the vermin has got used to the cage, then it can be set. The bait chosen depends on what species it is intended to catch and what it is feeding on. Dead rabbits, sheep, eggs and corn can all be used. White bread may also be taken, especially by rooks.

Smaller single catch cages of a different design can be used to catch magpies, etc., and should be baited with eggs or a dead rabbit.

Cage traps for animals are usually made from strong wire panels and are mainly used for feral cats and mink. Smaller ones can be successful for small animals, particularly squirrels. The latter are usually caught by using maize as a bait, which often proves attractive to jays as well.

The larger cage traps are often open-ended with a trip release mechanism in the centre on which is hung the bait. Fresh remains of small animals or birds, offal or fresh fish can be used.

The Keeper's Gibbet

The old-fashioned keeper's gibbet, where vermin was hung up, is **not** to be recommended. Nor is it a good idea to hang vermin up where it has been caught, although leaving a stoat laid on top of the tunnel it was caught in may very well draw another one to the trap. Public feeling runs high against the killing of any animal, whatever its habits. Therefore, to display dead vermin does nothing but create ill-feeling towards gamekeeepers and shooting in general. Added to this, hanging up the catches nearby will pinpoint the situation of the trap or snare. It may then be removed or damaged by those who do not understand the need for predator control.

List of Winged Predators

CROW (Carrion and Hooded)

Crows are the most consistently harmful of winged predators. They are cunning, intelligent and persistent. Unlike rooks, crows are not gregarious and a pair will stake out a large territory. Once resident, they will make an enormous incursion on songbird and game population alike. A pair of crows will systematically search for every nest, from which the eggs will be taken and sucked out. The discovery of emptied shells beneath trees is more often than not proved to be the work of a pair of crows. Young chicks are taken as well. Hooded crows, which are generally to be found in Scotland and Ireland, will also attack lambs or weakened sheep. Their vile habit of removing the eyes from still living creatures makes them unpopular with shepherds.

Crows should never be allowed to nest on a shoot. If a pair have remained undetected and have nested, then this should be located as soon as possible. The nest resembles a squirrels drey and is built high in a tree or, in some areas, on cliffs. If only one parent is dealt with, the other will continue to feed the young. Once aware of danger in the vicinity, the pair may be reluctant to return to the nest. A method often used to confuse this intelligent bird is for two people to go to the nesting site. One will then leave while the other remains hidden to deal with the returning bird.

If weather conditions permit, a sitting hen can sometimes be shot on the nest if it is moonlight at night. Lamping as such, though, is deemed illegal.

Luring the crow within shooting distance can also be successful. Mimicking the call and then throwing a dead crow into the air to arouse the curiosity may work in bringing one within gunshot. Decoying is also practised, using stuffed or imitation crows, cats, or owls, etc.

Cage trapping is the other method available anmd should be baited with eggs or carrion. In Scotland, where hooded crows are present, a dead sheep may prove an attractive bait.

3.14 Pigeon decoys set out on stubble

Coot and Moorhens (Waterhen)

Coots and moorhen can be a nuisance if too numerous, by eating food put out for game, by grazing winter corn and by sometimes stealing eggs or young chicks. They are quite easily shot or trapped and often find their way into catchers set for pheasants. They are protected by law from 1st February until 31st August.

Jackdaw

This corvid is smaller than the crow and has a grey patch at the back of the head. It, too, steals both eggs and young chicks and can also be a nuisance in open top laying pens by stealing food, particularly pellets. It nests most commonly in hollow trees and can often be ambushed as it leaves via the small entrance hole.

The main method of control is by cage trapping when bread may be used as an alternative bait to meat, eggs or grain.

Jay

Jays can at times be as destructive as the other corvids, but generally they are regarded with a little more tolerance by keepers. Their harsh warning cry can prove useful when they indicate the presence of some other predator. Jays can be dealt with by methods previously mentioned and are often caught in catchers set for grey squirrels or pheasants. Maize in particular, is attractive. In a year when there are few acorns, a laden oak tree will attract jays from a great distance. Numbers are often increased during the winter by migratory visitors in the South.

Magpie

Magpies are considered by many to be second to the crow in doing most harm on a shoot. Their numbers seem to be increasing, due no doubt to their adaptation to living within towns where they are left to breed undisturbed. In these suburban areas the effect on local song bird populations is dramatic and the magpie's presence should be discouraged whenever possible. It is also responsible for extensive damage to game bird populations and will destroy nests and kill chicks.

Cage traps, decoying and calling are methods of control and the nests of breeding pairs should be located and destroyed. The domed nest is often built in a thorn bush, so not only will woodland need to be searched, but also overgrown hedges.

During winter and early spring, groups of magpies band together. If a communal roosting place can be discovered, they can be dealt with when flighting in at evening time.

Rook

Rooks are very often wrongly called crows. Young ones are difficult to tell apart, but a mature rook is readily identified by an area of white skin around the base of the beak. In common with the crow, they can cause serious losses to nests and young broods. Rooks can also be very troublesome in open-topped laying pens and may account for the loss of hundreds, if not thousands of eggs, during the laying season. An inspection of the empty egg shells beneath surrounding trees will reveal the extent of the thieving that has taken place from within the pen.

Generally, rooks nest in communities and traditional rook shoots are held during early May when the young first leave the nests. To begin with, they sit out on surrounding branches and can then be dealt with. Using a .22 rifle is a cheap and efficient method.

Other methods of control, besides those previously mentioned for other species, are to keep the parents off their partly incubated eggs long enough for the embryo to become chilled and die. This may require permission, if local bylaws ban the use of 'bangers' at night. Few rookeries are conveniently situated in the middle of a keeper's beat to enable this method to be applied. Where it is possible, rope bangers placed in oil drums which have had the bottoms removed should be hung as high up in the trees as possible for all of one night.

Rooks often congregate in huge numbers to roost in certain woods during the winter. Their droppings can build up and kill off the vegetation beneath, and their presence is usually unacceptable to pheasants. Shooting on their flight lines may be possible at times. Some, too, may be shot when pigeons are being decoyed on laid corn. Rooks have a more varied diet than crows and, for this reason, are less harmful overall. They are popular with farmers when they search the fields for harmful soil pests, but unpopular when they steal grain.

Starlings

Like rooks, starlings often roost in communes and have a similar effect on a wood, making it unattractive for pheasants. There is also the risk of disease being spread, as many of the winter population are migratory visitors. Flares fired over them as they come in to roost may prove effective in moving them from the area.

Species That are Protected by Law

Most species of birds of prey are damaging to game birds, but it is illegal to kill them by any method. Some, such as the little owl and the kestrel, were numbered amongst the enemies of the gamekeeper when open rearing field methods were employed. A change in rearing conditions has lessened the threat of damage although, no doubt, some wild chicks still fall foul of their attentions. Others still remain as unwelcome visitors to any shoot and when resident can cause considerable losses.

Tawny Owls will freely take advantage of some easy living to be had from the confines of the release pens. They hunt at night and the discovery of a few headless corpses with claw marks on their backs next morning will reveal their attentions. They will often return to a kill.

Buzzards and Harriers are both to be found in open spaces. The lazy flight as they drift on the wind is deceiving. Their keen eyesight and speed of attack make them lethal killers. Their appearance on a shoot day can disrupt a grouse or partridge drive. Harriers, in particular, are most unwelcome residents on a grouse moor during the breeding season.

Sparrowhawks are fearless hunters, regularly attacking birds as large, if not larger, than themselves. They descend at lightning speed on their victims. The hen being larger than the male probably accounts for the majority of attacks on the larger birds. Pigeons are often caught and may be left half eaten and surrounded by plucked out feathers. Pheasant poults up to about nine weeks of age are also at risk and are especially vulnerable in a release pen to which a sparrow hawk may make regular visits. Adult partridges are also sometimes attacked and losses may be incurred to breeding pairs. A sparrowhawk will also return to a kill.

Birds of prey were at one time caught by placing traps on the top of posts or poles. This practice was known as pole trapping, but is now illegal.

Pigeons

Keepers are often called upon when pigeons are causing excessive damage to agricultural crops. They descend in vast numbers to gorge themselves on laid corn, newly sown grain or peas, and rape during the winter and spring. There are usually plenty of offers to help with the shooting and it is one way of saying thank you to beaters or pickers up who have helped during the shooting season. There are other unknown people who may phone or call in the hope of getting some shooting, but it is as well to choose carefully who is allowed on the estate. They will be in a position of trust, so it is as well to be wary.

The popular method of pigeon shooting is by decoying where they are feeding.

A hide should be built, preferably along a hedge or fence, using bales, fresh cut branches or camouflaged netting. The gun inside must be well hidden for pigeons are sharp-eyed and the slightest sign of anything abnormal will make them keep well clear of the area. Decoys, whether man-made models, or, better still, freshly shot pigeons, should be placed about twenty five yards out from the hide in a natural pattern. They should be placed facing the wind. Care must be taken not to shoot racing pigeons, which can often be identified by the presence of white primary feathers in the wing.

Pigeons can also be shot on flight lines, either between feeding areas or when they fly in to roost at night. Sometimes towers are constructed so that the gun is high up amongst the tree tops.

Various other deterrents are used in an effort to keep pigeons off crops. Strips of polythene, scarecrows, sirens and bangers are all employed.

The most commonly used is the gas gun which is operated from a gas bottle. It is adjusted to fire every few minutes throughout daylight hours. Either a manual switch or a time clock is used to turn it off and on. Pigeons soon get used to these regular bangs, so consequently it is advisable to move the guns to different parts of the field at intervals.

Pigeons can be a great nuisance to keepers on feed rides. They soon get used to coming when the pheasants are fed and will consume vast quantities of grain. Straw spread along the ride will make it more difficult for them to find it.

Feral pigeons are known to carry disease and their numbers need to be controlled. However, identification of these, apart from genuine racing pigeons, is difficult.

List of Mammalian Vermin

Cats Feral cats are ruthless hunters and can decimate game bird populations if they are uncontrolled. They can breed at an alarming rate and domestic cats very easily adapt to life in the wild. If they confined their attentions to rats and mice only, gamekeepers would less resent their presence on a shoot. But during the nesting season particularly, they can take a large toll of sitting birds and young chicks. A cat is usually deemed feral by a keeper if it is more than twenty five yards from its owner's garden, a fact which has caused many an argument! It must not be forgotten, though, that a cat is a lethal killer and that it is a gamekeeper's duty to protect his birds.

The favourite haunts of a feral cat are disused barns and straw stacks. When larger birds are killed, a cat will usually leave the wings, legs and gizzard where it has eaten its victim.

Shooting can be successful, as can cage traps baited with offal or other bait.

Coypu Coypu are large guinea pig-like rodents that are vegetarian. Although causing no harm to the gamekeeper, they may be caught in one of his traps. The presence of coypu should be reported to the Ministry of Agriculture, who are at present running an eradication scheme.

Coypu are found near water and are usually trapped in cage traps baited with root vegetables or apples. These traps are placed on banks or on rafts floating on the water near to the banks.

Deer Deer control is occasionally left to the keeper, but more often is let out to paying individuals. The keeper may, however, be involved with skinning the carcase and, in the case of a wounded beast, he may be asked to use his dogs to search for it. Deer stalking is dealt with in a separate chapter.

Deer are mainly unpopular with foresters for the tree damage they cause. They can also indirectly be a nuisance to keepers, especially when setting snares, and deer may also raid feed hoppers and game crops. A check for deer should be made inside of large release pens before the wire is pegged down and the gates closed. It may be as well to run a dog through first because one trapped inside will play havoc with the wire netting when it attempts to escape. Using a dog to work the pen out may also dislodge a fox or a cat that may have taken up residence.

Should the keeper be left to deal with deer, a suitable rifle must be used. Deer were once driven towards standing guns using shotguns, but this is now illegal.

Dogs Although not appearing on official lists of predators, uncontrolled dogs can be a real menace to some gamekeepers. They will kill and disturb game birds and deer. Many owners are completely unaware of the damage and disturbance their dogs can cause and, when it eventually returns home, assume that it 'has just had a nice run through the woods'.

Irresponsible owners are a menace and in some areas rate high on a keeper's list of undesirables. It is not only dogs that are allowed to roam freely from home that are troublesome, but also the ones that are taken out for a walk and allowed to hunt. A keeper knows better than anyone how wrong the favourite reply of 'he wasn't doing any harm' is when he requests the owner to keep the dog under control.

A keeper is only legally entitled to destroy a dog if it is causing damage to livestock contained within a pen and there is no alternative way of preventing it. There is no other legal right for a keeper to shoot a dog if it is killing his game. Recently the law has extended the right to protect sheep more fully.

3.15 Night shooting rabbits is the most efficient means of control

It is difficult for a keeper to differentiate between a dog that is allowed to hunt by an irresponsible owner and a much loved pet that has accidentally escaped from the garden when the gate has been left open. It is little wonder that keepers sometimes take matters into their own hands if they are constantly plagued by the attentions of roaming dogs.

Sometimes errant dogs are caught in fox snares. Usually they are held around the leg and they bark. It is suggested that the miscreant is taken to the local police station which does not usually welcome stray dogs. The owner then has the inconvenience of collecting the animal, the knowledge that its whereabouts have been recorded on a shoot, and hopefully a stern lecture from the officer in charge.

Fox Volumes could, and have, been written about the fox. Viewed with a god-like reverence by some individuals and looked upon as an unprecedented pest by others. The fox is the most lethal of killers, and no one knows better than a keeper what harm it can cause. Anyone who has personally witnessed the mass slaughter of pheasant poults in or around a release pen can retain much liking for such an animal. Poultry, lambs and young deer are all at risk. The fox, in many instances, kills for fun. No keeper will believe the naturalist who claims that foxes live mainly on mice and beatles, especially when he has discovered sitting pheasants or partridges pulled from their nests and the eggs destroyed.

There are many methods of control available, but in instances where the employer or landlord is a hunting man, or the public have access to the site, great care must be taken. Whatever the position, control over fox numbers is very necessary. Fox hunting is carried out from October until April and if hounds are given permission to hunt over the estate, a keeper must be prepared to tolerate the odd fox on his beat during the winter months. It is often argued that wounded birds will be killed quickly instead of suffering a lingering death if there is a fox present. In actual fact, the damage to game stocks at this time of the year is minimal compared with that during the nesting and rearing season.

The fox mates around Christmas time, or just after, and is likely to travel around during this period. The cubs are born underground from March onwards and, at first, the vixen will lay with them. Later, as the cubs grow stronger, the vixen will move them about, sometimes utilising disused rabbit holes and badger setts. At this stage the cubs lose their chocolate baby fur and it is replaced with the familiar red or sandy shade. Colours vary, as does the existence of a white tip to the brush. White markings are occasionally found on the chest if the underside is dark grey. Some people say that the dog fox only has a white tip to its tail, but this is not always so. When the cubs are growing, an increasing amount of damage is done to game bird stocks as this usually coincides with the nesting and hatching time. Realisation of the severity will become apparent if a fox earth is discovered that has been inhabited for several weeks. Remains of game, poultry, rabbits, hares, lambs and deer are all likely to be found. The dog fox also hunts for the family and food provided often exceeds that which is consumed. Foxes are unclean in their habits, remains of kills and their droppings will litter the vicinity of the occupied earth. It is this which identifies the occupants apart from badgers, which are much cleaner animals.

Foxes spend much of the day laying on top of the ground and older cubs and adults will make use of bracken beds, plantations and fields of standing corn for this purpose. It is a wise precaution at harvest time to visit the harvest field if there is a suspicion of a litter of cubs on the shoot. Preference is often shown for standing wheat. This is also the time of the year when foxes will be on the move, especially if there is cub hunting in the vicinity, which is intended to split the litters up.

A fox usually kills larger game birds either by biting the head off or by biting across the back. Sometimes the tooth marks are only visible when the bird is closely examined. Carcasses are often part buried or left scattered over a wide area. The tell-tale trail of feathers and broken and eaten eggs would suggest the work of a fox taking a sitting hen from her nest.

Snares are the most efficient method of control. They can be used at all times of the year and are forever laying in wait. Should a vixen be caught in the spring she should be carefully examined. If the fur is bared off and she is full of milk, she will have a litter of cubs in close proximity. Time should be devoted to searching every possible place and destroying them as quickly as possible. If a vixen has begun to dry up and her fur to grow again, then she will either have older cubs or possibly already have lost them. Once again, every effort must be made to locate the litter and once it has been discovered, it should be dealt with immediately. It is useless to leave the job until the following day as the other parent will have returned during the night and very likely moved the cubs.

Foxes caught in winter may provide extra pocket money when skinned and their pelts sold.

When a fox is suspected of laying up in a particular area, driving towards standing guns is suggested. Care must be taken to stand the guns down wind of the area and they must remain silent and inconspicuous. A team of beaters should then advance towards them. Any likely breaking points such as hedges, must be adequately covered and safety should be borne in mind. Heavy shot should be used.

Foxes can also be called up within shot by mimicking the squeal of a rabbit. A small piece of polystyrene dampened and rubbed against glass is extremely effective for this purpose. As they are predominantly nocturnal, foxes can also occasionally be accounted for when night shooting for rabbits.

On open ground, such as moorland, lurchers may be used to catch foxes that have been disturbed. A big, strong type of dog is required with sufficient jaw power to kill. Lamping at night using a rifle can also be practical.

The use of spring traps in which to catch foxes is now illegal and baited cage traps are of dubious value. Box traps are sometimes used when there is only one hole from which a fox may make an exit if cornered underground.

Gassing is most useful in the spring to deal with litters underground, although it can be used at any time when a fox is known to be occupying a bury. Earths should be checked frequently from early March until June so that litters can be quickly come to terms with. When it has been established that foxes, and not badgers, are in residence, then the holes should be gassed and filled in as soon as possible. Great care must be taken when handling gas.

In earths, other holes and stacks of bales where gassing is impractical, terriers can be used to evict the tenants. The holes should either be netted or, alternatively, foxes can be shot as they bolt. Once again, great care must be taken to avoid accidents and injury to man or dog. A good terrier is invaluable in areas where digging is difficult and gassing impossible. The dog should be selected from working stock; he should be narrow enough around the chest to be encircled by the hands. A terrier is more useful if it will bay at a fox and cause it to bolt, rather than to attempt to kill it underground. In hill areas, a slightly larger terrier is sometimes preferred that is capable of killing a fox.

Hares Hares are classed as game; however, they may be killed at any time, but can only be offered for sale between August and February inclusive. On moorlands and unenclosed areas, they may only be shot between December 11 (July 1 in Scotland) and March 31. *(see page 326)*

Numbers of hares have been declining in recent years, no doubt in part due to the increased use of agricultural sprays, in particular herbicides, that are used on stubbles to kill off growth. However, in some areas, hares still need to be controlled and, other than night shooting, the usual method is to hold an annual hare drive. This is normally arranged during February when a large army of beaters drive areas of hundreds of acres of ground towards a line of standing guns. Experienced guns decline the opportunity to shoot hares from the beating line, with the knowledge that it is difficult to carry one or more over a distance of a mile or across sticky plough.

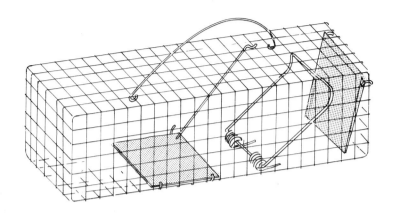

FENN HEAVY DUTY MINK TRAP (also larger for feral cats)

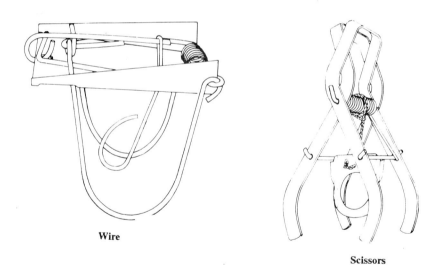

Wire

Scissors

MOLE TRAPS

3.16 TRAPS

(Courtesy Fenn & Co., Redditch, Worcs.)

No. 4 or 5 shot is recommended for hare shooting, and a game licence is required.

Hunting hares with beagles is another popular sport, and many keepers have to play host to these hounds once or twice in the course of the year.

Coursing with lurchers or greyhounds is becoming increasingly popular. When organised properly and legitimately, little can be said against it, but so often it is this type of dog that is run illicitly by gypsies and the like that gives coursing a bad name. When used without permission, this constitutes poaching and it is not only hares that are hunted, but deer as well.

Professionally organised coursing meetings are very similar to grouse or partridge shoots. Beaters are employed to take in a large area of ground. Most are issued with flags. As with grouse and partridge shooting, these flags should only be shown if a hare attempts to break out and kept out of sight at other times. Hares are driven towards a hedge or narrow belt of trees behind which the coursing dogs are waiting. These are run in pairs and are unleashed simultaneously some distance behind the hare. The man who releases the dogs is known as the 'slipper'. The dogs are judged on their skill at turning the hare and receive no points for a kill. Any hare that does not appear fully fit is not coursed and the majority escape unharmed.

Hares do not directly cause damage, so far as keepers are concerned, although they can be a nuisance if it is wished to set snares for foxes. The need for control is usually deemed necessary by the crop damage they cause and the harm they do to young trees.

Hedgehogs Hedgehogs have recently been afforded some protection by the *Wildlife and Countryside Act* (1981). Certain methods of control which include the use of all traps, snares, poisons and gas, and the use of lamps at night, are now prohibited. This, in effect, leaves daytime shooting as a practical method of control. It is not stated how it is possible to prevent a hedgehog entering a trap specifically set for other ground vermin.

Their nuisance value on a wild bird shoot should not be under- estimated. Other predators are often apportioned the blame that is due to a hedgehog. It is during the nesting season that most damage occurs, when birds will be dragged off nests and the eggs scattered and eaten. Partridges, particularly, are vulnerable to attack, and a spell of dry weather, when slugs and snails are less prolific, may increase the risk. Larger birds are often left partially eaten from the rear end.

The hedgehog is nocturnal, and hibernates during the winter months. Occasionally a group will be discovered and can be destroyed; if not, a concentrated effort needs to be made during the spring.

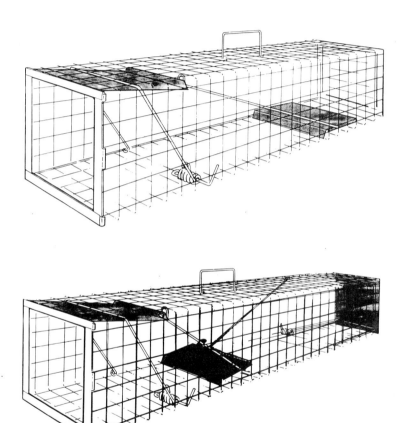

3.17 RABBIT CAGE TRAPS

(Courtesy Patrick Pinker)

Mink Mink are ever increasing and, to those unfamiliar with the predator, their kills may be blamed onto a stoat. They are nocturnal, often black in colour, and resemble a large ferret in appearance.

Mink are normally found within range of water and will kill for pleasure. They can cause serious losses to game birds, particularly to duck, or in the vicinity of a release pen. Bodies may be found bitten at the back of the head and an attempt may have been made to drag the kill through the surrounding wire netting. Inspection of river banks and muddy places may reveal paw prints and other indications. Every effort should be made to eradicate this animal as it is extremely harmful to all kinds of wild life.

Cage traps are the most efficient method, and baited spring traps may also be used in tunnels, drains, etc.

Traps should be set near water or drains, etc., and should be baited with fresh offal or fish.

Moles Moles only cause indirect harm to gamekeepers and usually it is when molehills appear on the employer's lawn that the keeper's services are requested. They can cause occasional damage to partridge nests by accidental disturbance, and mole runs may also be used by weasels.

There are several designs of mole traps marketed which are placed in the mole runs; these are located by testing the ground with a stick.

When moles are a serious problem, a licence may be obtained from the Ministry of Agriculture which authorises the purchase of strychnine. This is sprinkled onto large, freshly dug earth worms which are then introduced into the mole runs. Care must obviously be taken when handling this dangerous poison.

Phostoxin fumigation tablets are recommended also for use in mole runs underground.

Rabbit The rabbit must be classed as one of the world's greatest survivors. Since its introduction here by the Normans, it has been the diet of both man and carnivores. It has survived countless methods of control and a plague of myxomatosis that very nearly eradicated it from the British Isles in the 1950s. Through its ability to rapidly reproduce, it has caused millions of pounds worth of damage to agriculture and still it remains one of the most common wild animals in Britain.

Rabbit control is generally left to the keeper, sometimes assisted by farm staff. The sale of rabbits is often one of the keeper's perks.

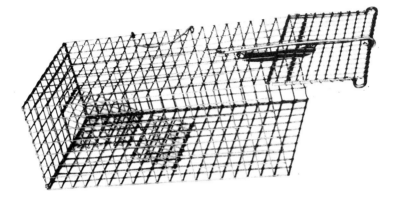

FULLER RAT TRAP

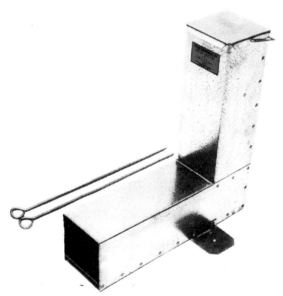

FULLER POISON HOPPER

3.18 TRAPS

(Courtesy Fuller Engineering Ltd., Worthing, West Sussex)

Coursing, traps and snares are sometimes used, and ferreting is a popular sport dealt with in Chapter 16. An assessment should be made of the trust-worthiness of anyone offering to go ferreting.

Rabbit control is best conducted in winter and early spring, before breeding commences. Ground vegetation is short then, and holes can be more easily located and rabbits sighted.

Gassing is a popular method of control, but there is no monetary gain to leaving dead rabbits underground. This can be combined with driving, i.e. 'top rabbiting', but care must be taken to ensure that every hole is filled, or else the rabbits will go to ground before reaching the forward waiting guns. Dogs can be useful for evicting rabbits from dense cover, and a terrier can be as useful as a gun dog for this purpose.

Top rabbiting can also be conducted when rabbits have been 'stunk out', i.e. using diesel or some other strong smelling substance, to force the rabbits to vacate their holes and lay out on top of the ground.

A toll of rabbits can be taken with a rifle in the evenings when they come out to feed, but by far the best method of shooting is night shooting from a vehicle. The beam of the headlights or torch dazzles the rabbits and they can be picked off with either a rifle or a shotgun. The rabbits will hold better in the lights when it is dark, with no moon, but they dislike strong winds. Certain safety precautions should be adhered to and it is wise to choose shooting companions carefully. The driver of the vehicle also needs to be familiar with the ground. It is advisable to notify neighbours and the local police of the intention to shoot, and areas adjacent to houses should be worked as early as possible so as not to cause undue disturbance. A large number of rabbits can be accounted for in an evening by an experienced team.

Rats Rats, like rabbits, are responsible for thousands of pounds worth of damage every year, added to which is the hazard of them carrying disease. There is one in particular, Leptospirosis, that can kill dogs if they are infected. This, and other diseases can also be transmitted to man, and care should be taken when handling rats to avoid direct contact.

Not only do rats eat and foul vast quantities of food intended for game, but they can cause serious losses during the breeding season. They readily eat meat and will eat whatever part of a bird that they can pull through holes in boards or wire netting. Rats will eat eggs which they will roll away from a nest.

During dry weather, rats will live in hedgerows and, in autumn, will feed on corn left from harvest, beech masts, etc. They can also cause noticeable damage to freshly drilled seed corn or beans by digging it up and eating it. In winter, rats tend to move into buildings and stacks.

There are obvious signs of rat occupation wherever it is. They use regular runs, and these can easily be seen between holes. There are usually piles of droppings that can be readily identified.

Tunnel traps set along banks and hedgerows will account for a number of rats throughout the year.

Where heavy infestations have built up, poisoning is the most efficient method of control (see page 35)' . It must be emphasised that poisoning must be continued until there are no longer any signs of habitation. It is useless and harmful not to do the job properly. Every precaution must be taken to safeguard the poison from livestock, domestic pets and children. In some areas, rats are resistant to Warfarin, so other poisons must be selected. Local advice should be sought.

Ferrets, shooting, snaring and terriers are all other methods of control employed against the rat.

Local populations fluctuate from year to year and there seems to be a general opinion that there is considerable movement of numbers. Rats appear to be most prolific on lighter land where corn is grown extensively.

Every effort should be made to eradicate rats and regular inspections should be made of farm buildings, straw stacks and rubbish dumps. Baiting points should be operated permanently and particular attention should be paid to feed stores.

A very effective mouse poison is marketed which contains Calciferol and Warfarin mixed with bird seed.

Squirrels Grey squirrels are much more harmful than the red squirrels that they have almost eradicated. They do extensive damage to forestry and steal grain put out for game birds. Their habit of gnawing and chewing can also be expensive. Squirrels will steal eggs and eat young birds. To all intents and purposes, they are a climbing rat, but are cleaner in their habits.

The population fluctuates over the years, but their numbers should be controlled whenever possible.

Tunnel traps account for a fair proportion, and cage traps baited with maize can be useful.

Shooting can be good sport when a party is organised to go drey poking during the winter months. Sectional alloy poles can be slotted together to form up to a forty foot (12m.) length. Each drey should be systematically destroyed and the occupants shot. A single gun will experience difficulty, as

3.19 Motorised pump for gassing rabbits

(Courtesy Patrick Pinker Ltd.)

3.20 Cymag hand pump

squirrels are very cunning and hide craftily on the opposite side of a tree. Throwing a stone or piece of wood may be sufficient to cause some movement of position. Terriers can be useful assistants when shooting squirrels, especially as a squirrel will often disappear down a hole when forced onto the ground. Gun dogs should never be used, as a bite from a squirrel can be severe and result in a dog becoming hard mouthed.

Warfarin poison is specified as being suitable to use for the destruction of grey squirrels. There are certain restrictions covering the poison concentration, method of presentation and the counties in which it is permitted. It may not be used in Scotland where the red squirrel still exists. Specially designed dispensers should be used to prevent accesss by other animals and birds, although the latter appear to be resistant to Warfarin. Pre-baiting is advised, and whole maize may assist in attracting the squirrels to the hopper in the first instance. Wheat is recommended for mixing with the poison.

Care should be taken when dealing with live squirrels, as not only do they have sharp claws, but also very sharp, strong teeth which they can, and do, use to good effect.

Stoats Stoats are readily distinguished from weasels by the fact that they are at least twice the size and have a black tip to the tail. They are fearless predators, frequently attacking rabbits several times larger than themselves. Kills are identified as the work of a stoat by inspecting the back of the skull for teeth marks. Damage can be caused both to eggs and sitting birds. At a later stage, attacks may be made on pheasants in the release pen and, on occasions, killing appears to be the result of pleasure rather than hunger, resulting in a score or more dead poults being discovered. Sometimes a stoat will drag its kill to the edge of the pen and will often return to its victim.

Litters of stoats can be quite large, and they stay together in a family unit during the summer. If the whereabouts of a litter is discovered, every effort should be made to come to terms with them. Spring traps are effective. The stoat can also be squeaked within very close range if it is unaware of the presence of a human being. Old tree stumps are particularly favourite haunts, and a stoat will soon go to ground in a rabbit hole when pressed.

In some areas of Great Britain the stoat changes to white or part-coloured during the winter.

Weasels Weasels are not quite so harmful as stoats, but nevertheless they can take a toll at nesting time. Being small, they can make use of mole runs and rat runs underground to remain undetected. When the open field rearing system was popular, weasels could be a great nuisance when they turned their attention to the coops of young chicks.

In areas where rats are plentiful, they may form a large percentage of a weasel's diet.

Trapping or shooting as for stoats are recommended methods of control.

Badgers are now protected by law and must not be killed by any method. Exceptions in certain areas are made only with the authority of the Ministry of Agriculture.

Badgers are nocturnal and can cause damage to nesting birds. Occasionally they will turn their attentions to release pen sites. Fox earths must be carefully inspected to make sure that badgers are not in occupation before gassing, etc. (see paragraph on the fox). On no account should a terrier be entered to a badger. Apart from it being illegal, a badger has very strong jaws and can cause serious injuries to the dog.

Hazards to Game

To conclude this chapter, some mention must be made of the harmful effects of modern agricultural policies and machinery. Throughout the year, farm work creates a potential hazard to game stock, both directly and indirectly. Farm management must be sympathetic to the needs of game if wild stocks are to flourish, and with understanding between both parties, there need be no loss of profit. The timing of operations is often of most importance. The mowing of verges, if either brought forward by a couple of weeks, or delayed by a couple of weeks, can have a noticeably beneficial effect on nesting. It is so frustrating for the keeper to have walked his hedges and banks, noted the nests and then have to watch the flail mower driven along and destroy them. If the roadside verges were cut back one width before nesting had commenced, the keeper would welcome this. Likewise, if further cutting could be delayed, until the bulk of hatching was over, say early July, then this, too, would cause no aggravation.

Combining late in the evening, or after dark, can cause serious losses if poults from a nearby release pen have got into the habit of jukking in the standing corn. Co-operation, by ensuring that adjacent fields to release pens are combined during daylight, costs nothing to the farm, but can count for a lot with the keeper.

Sprays are an inevitable hazard, both in themselves and the effect they have in killing off insects that form such a vital part of the diet of newly hatched game. Co-operation in this department need not cost anything. By selecting sprays and dressings that are not harmful to game, the keeper will be happier and the profits are no less. Spraying herbicides into hedge bottoms and banks during nesting time is another unnecessary hazard that game has to contend with. The resultant loss of cover may not only cause the hen bird to desert the nest, but also leaves the nest open and more obvious to predators.

Perhaps the most damaging agricultural operations insofar as nesting birds are concerned is silage cutting. This is usually conducted first during late May, when a high percentage of pheasants will be sitting. Lulled by a false sense of security into choosing the long grass as an ideal nesting site, they are at the mercy of the fast moving machinery. The tendency of a pheasant to squat instead of run when faced with danger results in few surviving.

Throughout the shooting season, co-operation is still required to prevent disappointing results on a shoot day. Stubbles that are inconveniently left on boundaries will entice birds away from the middle. Hedge cutting in operation the day a partridge beat is to be shot may make handling difficult. Fresh drilled corn may prove more attractive to pheasants than wheat fed in a particular cover that is to be driven.

Forestry work, too, should be included in the examples of co- operation. Not only in winter time, where pheasant drives are planned, but also during the nesting season.

For game, the hazards incurred by modern farming techniques are many, but with communication and co-operation between the keeper and the farm manager, the damage and disagreements should be kept to a minimum.

4

Egg Production and Incubation

Recommended Reading
Game Conservancy Advisory Booklet No. 5

INCUBATION PERIODS
PARTRIDGE 23 days (English 24 days)
PHEASANT 24 days
DUCK 28 days
HEN OR BANTAM 21 days

Partridge and pheasant eggs are usually treated the same. They are put in an incubator (setter) for the first 21 days and then transferred to another incubator (hatcher) for the last 3 days. Temperature is maintained between 99.5-100 degrees F (37.5-37.8 degrees C). Duck eggs are transferred at 24 days. The same temperature is needed, but humidity levels must be kept higher throughout. If French partridge eggs are to be hatched in the same machine as pheasants' eggs they should be set in the incubators 18-24 hours after the pheasant eggs are put in as they have a slightly shorter incubation period.

A broody hen will incubate seventeen pheasants eggs or fourteen duck eggs, on average.

A medium sized bantam is capable of taking twelve to fifteen partridge eggs. N.B. Legislation is likely that permits the release of only pure French partridge — hybrids will be prohibited.

4.1 Drop Catcher made from hazel sticks

4.2 A simply made wire netting catcher

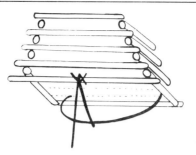

SINGLE CATCH – DROP OR BASKET CATCHER

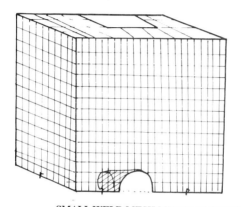

SMALL WELD MESH MULTI-CATCHER

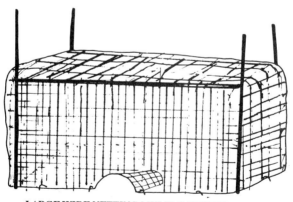

LARGE WIRE NETTING MULTI-CATCHER

DIAGRAM OF TYPES OF CATCHERS

Catching up

The catching up of breeding stock takes place normally after Christmas. Some keepers like to have their hen birds safely penned before the cock shoots are organised, while others prefer to leave catching up until the shooting season has finished and the pheasants have settled down.

Only first quality birds should be selected for breeding. Areas where late hatched poults were released are best avoided.

Methods of catching are dependent on the choice of the individual keeper and the number he is expected to catch. When only a few are required, a drop catcher is often the choice. This is made from hazel sticks or thin slats to form a catcher approximately two feet (60cms.) square and about twelve to fifteen inches (30- 40cms.) high. Access should be available from the top to remove the trapped bird. A coop will suffice, if available. One side is propped up with a trip release arrangement and corn is fed underneath. The pheasant, either when entering or feeding, will release the device and the catcher will fall down over the bird. The two disadvantages with this individual catcher are that only one bird is caught at a time and corn eaters, such as jays, squirrels and other small birds, may also trip the catcher.

Multi-catchers are much more frequently used. They are usually constructed to be at least four feet (120cms.) square and with one or more tunnels through which the birds can enter, but not escape. Suitable materials are battens, wire netting, weld mesh or even rearing pen sections. Less injury will be caused to pheasants when trapped if the mesh is large enough for them to get their heads through. The catcher must be securely pegged to the ground.

Whichever method of catching is used, the catchers should be placed in position and the pheasants allowed to feed freely beneath them for a few days prior to use.

When set up, they must be visited frequently and the trapped birds removed. Pheasants will panic when approached, so speed is essential when taking them out. A wedged stick to hold the top of the catcher closed can very quickly be removed. Pheasants must be handled carefully to prevent injury or the loss of feathers. Covering the top of the catcher will help to quieten them during the transfer from catcher to sack or crate.

It will be found that the majority of hen pheasants will be caught either early in the morning or in the evening.

All signs of disturbance such as loose feathers must be removed and fresh corn sprinkled inside and in the tunnels. The top must be securely fastened and pegs in the ground checked when the catcher is reset.

4.3 Walled gardens make ideal laying pens. Even when brailed pheasants will climb up into trees so care must be taken that they cannot escape

4.4 Laying pens often constructed with sheets of galvanised tin around the base to provide protection from the wind and to prevent the birds from pacing the wire in an effort to get out. Fir boughs in the foreground provide cover for the hens to lay beneath

4.5 English partridges for breeding are over-wintered and then paired up for laying

4.6 French partridges for breeding are often kept on wire

DIAGRAM SHOWING THE WAY IN WHICH A RING BRAIL IS PUT ON A PHEASANT'S WING

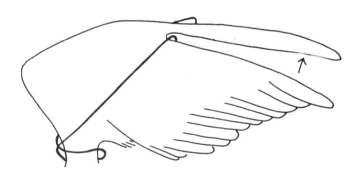

BRAILING FOR BIRDS IN OPEN PENS

If the birds are to be left in sacks, these should be well spread out on the ground and not over-filled. Otherwise birds should be transferred to crates.

French Partridges are best caught by a similar method where feeding areas have been established after release. These should be caught around Christmas time, as coveys may disperse after then. French partridges can often be caught in catchers set for pheasants if they have been feeding with them.

Quite often squirrels and jays, as well as other vermin, will be caught in pheasant catchers, particularly if maize is used as bait.

A ratio of one cock pheasant to seven or eight hens is necessary, whatever type of laying pens are used. If French partridges are to be flockmated, then one cock will be needed for every three hens. English partridges are rarely bred successfully when caught up, and are always kept in pairs. If breeding stock is required, this should be retained and over-wintered from the previous season's young stock. Pairs should be selected in late winter; some couples may need to be changed as not all cocks and hens are compatible.

Laying Pens

When movable covered laying pens for pheasants are used, wing clipping or brailing is not essential. These small pens have several advantages, namely egg production is usually higher, eggs are safe from predators, vices such as egg eating or feather pecking can be dealt with easily, and fresh ground is regularly available. The disadvantages are ones of expense, both for the materials used and the extra labour involved. These sectional pens are usually 10 feet by 6 feet (3m. by 2m.) and contain seven hens and one cock bird. Sections can be dismantled, cleaned out and used for rearing pens for the last hatch of chicks or for releasing partridge.

Communal pens are usually constructed on open ground and often sheets of corrugated tin are placed around the bottom to provide some protection from the weather. The pen must be vermin proof and sufficiently large. Any number of birds can be penned. These permanent pens are less labour intensive, but there is a great risk of crows, etc. stealing the eggs and food. It may be difficult to collect the eggs if the cover is allowed to grow too dense.

Birds put in these open-topped pens will need to be brailed or to have one wing clipped. Brailing is a simple matter with the modern ring brails which are slipped over the wing and one or two primary feathers pulled through as illustrated. On no account must all the feathers be clipped from the wing. Without these, there is no protection for the back and serious injuries will be inflicted during the course of the breeding season. Half the wing feathers need to be clipped on one wing only to prevent the bird from flying.

4.7 Dirty eggs must be cleaned. A 'Rotomaid' egg washer is ideal for this purpose. Eggs are collected in the wire baskets which are them immersed.

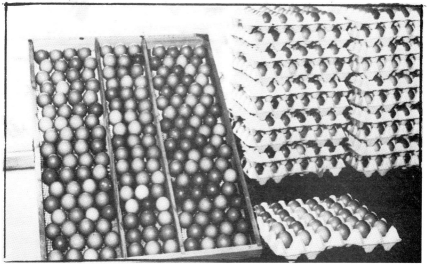

4.8 Pheasant eggs are best stored in papier mache egg trays. They are packed pointed end downwards in both the egg trays and the incubator trays

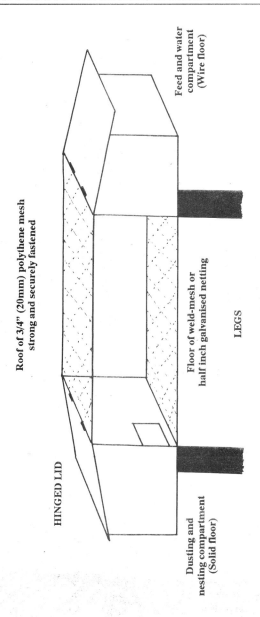

Feed and water compartment (Wire floor)

Roof of 3/4" (20mm) polythene mesh strong and securely fastened

Floor of weld-mesh or half inch galvanised netting

LEGS

HINGED LID

Dusting and nesting compartment (Solid floor)

Batteries can be constructed in units of five pens. Overall measurement is approximately 10ft x 6ft (3m x 2m), thus each pen is approximately 6ft (2m) long x 2ft (60cms) wide. The unit should stand well clear of the ground. Each pen houses one pair of partridges.

DIAGRAM OF PARTRIDGE LAYING PEN (BATTERY TYPE)

'Spex' can be inserted in the nostrils to prevent egg eating and feather pecking.

The spurs of the cock birds should be blunted, either by clipping the sharp points off, or using a de-beaker, to prevent damage to the hens.

The birds should be allowed plenty of time to settle down in the breeding pens before egg laying begins in early April. Pellets should be introduced, gradually at first, at the beginning of March. A good quality breeder's ration should be used.

The communal, or flock, pen should be decked with fir boughs or similar, to provide cover for the hens to lay beneath. Straw bales, sheets of corrugated tin, old oil drums or coops will suffice if fir is not available.

Only fit and healthy birds should have been selected for stock, but if there is any chance of gapes or other worms being present, then the flock should be treated accordingly prior to coming into lay.

A third method of penning is suitable for partridges. The battery system, where pairs are accommodated in wire floored cages, is most frequently used. This method has the added advantage over the other systems in that, as they are kept on wire, the partridges should have no contact with disease. French partridges are very prone to gapes, which can seriously affect egg produciton, and this risk is virtually eliminated by using the battery system. Cock and hen French partridges are very difficult to tell apart, which may make pairing a problem. The cock bird is generally broader and heavier than the hen. The knobbly spurs on the legs are some indication, as although often present on the hen, they are somewhat less developed.

Care of Eggs

Pheasants and French partridges usually begin to lay in late March or early April. English partridges may be as much as a month later. The breeding stock should be fed entirely on breeder's pellets by this time and, although the ration is claimed to provide sufficient calcium to produce strong shells, some keepers like to make oyster shell grit available. It is beneficial to provide flint grit at the same time.

Laying areas should be kept as clean as possible, although weather conditions often make this difficult. Straw should be used if necessary. The eggs should be picked up as often as possible and, when dirty, should be washed immediately in an approved egg sanitant. Instructions for use should be followed, and the addition of dairy grade hypochlorite at the rate of 1 fluid ounce per 2.5 gallons (30cc. to 12 litres) will be even more effective in killing harmful bacteria.

4.9 Hygienic plastic storage trays and egg washing system

(Courtesy of Hardwick Game Farm, Suffolk)

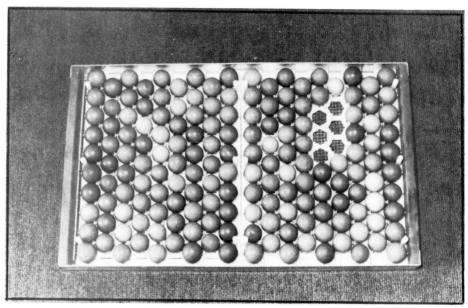

4.10 Plastic inserts make traying-up eggs much easier. 2-pheasant egg size and a partridge egg size are manufactured by Hardwick Game Farm, Suffolk

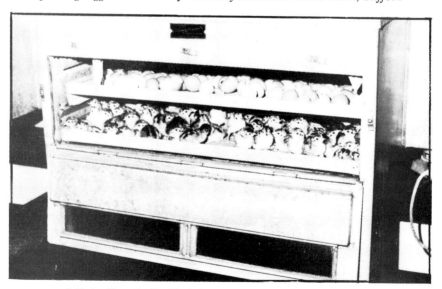

4.11 An 'Ironclad' still air incubator produces strong chicks

The solution should be kept slightly above the temperature of the egg (35 degrees C - 40 degrees C for 3 minutes is recommended) to draw the bacteria and chemicals out of the shell. A damp cloth should never be used, as this will quickly spread contamination from egg to egg. After washing, the eggs should be allowed to drain and dry before being stored pointed end down in egg trays. Cracked, misshapen and abnormally shelled eggs should be discarded. Eggs for hatching should be stored in a cool, humid place, preferably at a temperature of 50-60 degrees F (11-16 degrees C). Setting usually takes place weekly, but if eggs need to be kept longer, they should be turned daily. This can be done by tilting the trays one way for one day, and the other for the next.

If eggs have been transported, they should be rested for twenty four hours prior to setting.

The incubators should be serviced, scrubbed out, disinfected and fumigated before use. Cleanliness is essential at all times to prevent a build-up of disease. The temperature and humidity needed to hatch an egg provides the ideal environment in which bacteria breed. A separate incubator should be used for duck eggs as there is an increased risk of disease.

Eggs can be fumigated both before and during incubation, but great care must be taken not to damage the embryo. Accurately measured amounts of formalin and potassium permanganate are mixed to give off formaldehyde gas which will kill all micro organisms and bacteria. The gas is highly irritant, so any contact must be avoided. The amounts used are calculated from the size of the area to be fumigated. It must be worked out accurately, whether it is a small incubator or a large room. When eggs are fumigated after setting, they should be left long enough to be properly warmed through. But they must **NOT** be fumigated during the 24-96 hour period after setting or in the later stages of incubation. after the transfer stage.

Fumigation is an efficient method of sterilisation, but great care must be taken when done. It is best carried out last thing at night, when the fumes will have time to disperse before work needs to continue in the room. Instructions for fumigation should be carefully followed at all times.

Incubators

Forced air machines are generally used for the first 21 days of incubation before the eggs are transferred into still air machines for hatching. Game bird eggs are not as easy to hatch in incubators as poultry eggs. Partridge eggs are easiest, and an average hatch of 70-80% of all eggs set should be achieved. Pheasant eggs should give results between 60% and 70% and duck may be less than this. At all times the amount of humidity is of prime

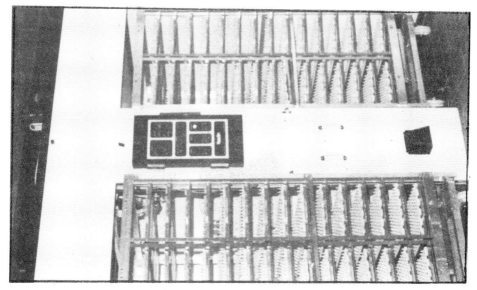

4.12 Large cabinet incubators are fitted with trolleys containing the integral egg trays which are simply wheeled in

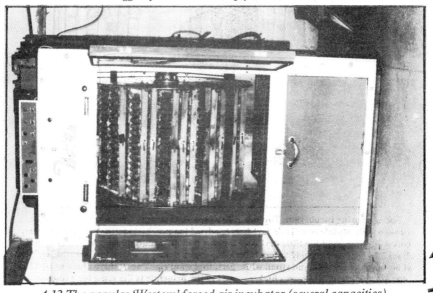

4.13 The popular 'Western' forced air incubator (several capacities)

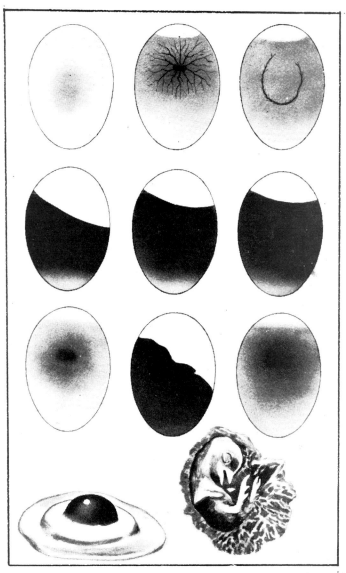

The egg during incubation: Top row (7th day) left, clear egg; centre, fertile egg; right, broken yolk. Middle row (14th day) left, egg dried too much - too little moisture; centre, correct drying; right too little drying - excessive moisture. Bottom row, left, dead embryo about 5th day; centre, ready to hatch 20th day, right, embryo died on about 14th day. Left, at bottom, the egg yolk and small white germinal spot; right, an embryo chick at 14-15th day of incubation These are chicken eggs, but the principle is the same for game birds.

Hand candling

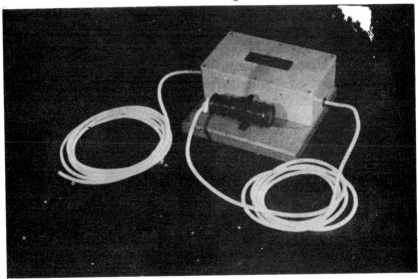

Candling machine

4.15 Egg Candling (see text)

(Courtesy Patrick Pinker)

importance and instructions for the machine used should be followed. Advice from fellow keepers should be sought, as local conditions may necessitate a slight deviation to the amount of water originally recommended.

A wet bulb thermometer can be made by making a tube of absorbent cloth, one end of which should be placed over the bulb of the thermometer and the other end should be dipped in a small bottle of distilled water which must be kept filled. The wick should be moistened and a reading of approximately 82 to 85 degrees F (29.5 degrees C) maintained. This can be done either by filling the water trays in the machine for so many days a week, or alternatively by keeping the trays filled permanently and limiting the area of water.

Eggs can be candled (shining a bright light through the eggs) to show the size of the air cell at different stages. This indicates the amount of water absorbed by the embryo inside. A certain size of air cell is needed at the 21 day stage for the chick to hatch successfully. Although recommendations are made, confusion can arise if different size air cells are apparent in the batch of eggs examined, as sometimes happens. There is no substitute for experience, and a detailed examination of hatching results will usually expose areas for improvement.

If only a very small number of eggs is to be hatched, a small still air incubator can be used throughout incubation. The manufacturer's instructions should be rigidly followed, particularly with regards to acquiring the correct level of humidity.

Larger forced air cabinet incubators are more commonly used (see diagram). These are usually fully automatic, being fixed with a very sensitive thermostat to control temperature levels and a mechanical turning gear which operates at intervals. If turning by hand is necessary, this should be done at least three times a day and preferably five. By turning them an odd number of times, the eggs will not be left on the same side overnight, which is usually the longest period they are left unturned.

The trays in cabinet setters are sometimes marked in a sequence of three colours. This is done because eggs are usually set weekly and remain in the setter for 21 days. They are then transferred into a hatcher and the trays refilled. The colour marking of tray positions is designed to balance the spread of fresh eggs or empty trays within the machine.

The temperature is maintained accurately by mercury contact thermometers to a tenth of a degree. The most commonly used contact thermometer is one that maintains a temperature of 99.7 degrees F, and any incubator should be kept between 99.5 and 100 degrees F (37.5-37.8 degrees C). In the smaller still air machines that may be run on gas, paraffin or electricity, such an accurate temperature is difficult to achieve. Often there are two thermometers in these, one above the eggs, and one below. The top one should be hung about two inches above the egg tray and the temperature controls adjusted to give a reading of 103. degrees F (39.7 degrees C). Slight natural fluctuations occur and it is unwise to alter the setting unless the temperature remains too high or too low over a period of several hours. The thermostat used in these smaller still air machines is usually a capsule type.

Large specially designed cabinet hatchers have accurate and easily adjusted thermostats.

Machines run below 99.5 degrees F (37.5 degrees C) will produce a delayed hatch and ones run above 100 degrees F (37.8 degrees C) will seriously affect hatchability. Chicks inside the shell can easily be killed by overheating.

Whichever type of machine is used, and there are many makes to choose from, the manufacturer's instructions should always be followed. Hatching game bird eggs is difficult, and some machines give better results than others.

Ventilation of the incubator or hatcher itself is important and may need to be increased as soon as the chicks have hatched. The room where the incubator or hatcher is sited can also be very important; not so much for forced air machines, but for avoiding fluctuating temperatures and draughts where still airs are situated. The changes of air inside these machines is caused by a convection process, and excessive heat and draughts will play havoc with this. The room should preferably be kept between 60 and 70 degrees F (16 and 21 degrees C) and well ventilated. Machines should not be placed where the sun will shine on them.

Candling is sometimes carried out when eggs are transferred at 21 days. Clear (infertile) eggs are discarded at this stage. Most setter trays are designed so that the eggs are packed with the pointed end downwards. They should be held in place with paper or cotton wool to prevent any movement. Some keepers pin a piece of plastic mesh over the top of the trays, as an added precaution against the eggs slipping out. Specially designed plastic inserts for setting trays are now available. These hold the eggs securely in position and greatly reduce the time and care needed when packing eggs.

Hatching

When the eggs are transferred to the hatcher they are laid on their sides and should not be turned after the 21st day. If a small still air machine is used with the heating element on one side, then it is a good idea to turn the tray round occasionally until hatching commences.

Hatching Stage 1
First Chip

Hatching Stage 2
Chick at work

Hatching Stage 3
Ready to emerge

Hatching Stage 4
Completion

4.16 Stages in hatching

Once the eggs begin to pip, the water containers inside should be filled up and the machine NOT opened until hatching is completed. Increased humidity and the steaming up of inspection windows is an indication that hatching is progressing satisfactorily.

Some keepers sprinkle water on the floor of the hatcher room to increase humidity during dry weather.

Better results occur if the chicks hatch all at the same time, instead of over a period of several hours. It is therefore best to separate stale eggs when set, as these may be slightly delayed when hatching.

When it is judged that hatching is completed, the ventilation of the machine can be increased to allow the chicks sufficient oxygen and an opportunity to dry.

They should then be left overnight to gain strength.

Care must be taken when chicks are removed from the hatcher to avoid chilling. The transfer from incubator to brooder unit should be done as quickly as possible. If the chicks need to be sent for long distances, specially designed chick boxes must be used. Normally 34 pheasant chicks or 50 partridge chicks will remain warm and comfortable inside one of these for up to another 24 hours. Wood wool or shavings should be used in the bottom, but avoid using hay unless it is completely free from mould. Weak or deformed chicks should be culled.

When the hatchers are emptied, they should be thoroughly cleaned and disinfected before being re-heated in readiness for the next batch of eggs. Debris from the hatch should be buried or burned.

Pheasants need to be at least 20 weeks old before being mature enough to shoot. This must be borne in mind when working out the last day for setting eggs to shoot on a particular date.

Hatching with broodies

It is essential that a broody hen or bantam should be given no more eggs than she can comfortably cover. Broodies are extremely useful to have in reserve for odd clutches of eggs that are picked up because of desertion by the sitting bird or because the nest is otherwise at risk.

At one time all game birds eggs were hatched by broodies in long rows of sitting boxes. These boxes are not often available, but coops will do well as a substitute.

They should be placed in a shady position and preferably slightly raised to eliminate the risk of the nest becoming waterlogged.

4.17 Typical coops

4.18 Tethered hens released from Broody Boxes

A shallow hollow should be made in the ground and the nest shaped from good quality hay. Musty or mouldy hay must not be used.

The broody should be selected from healthy free range stock. Often a keeper keeps a few bantams for the sole purpose of having a broody available when needed, otherwise they may be difficult to come by when required. Silkie crosses or other traditional farmyard breeds are the most reliable.

The bird should be de-loused and introduced to the nest which contains dummy eggs. She shoould be left quiet except for the regular daily routine of removing her to feed, drink and empty herself. A cord should be attached to one leg so that she can be tethered to a stick when she is off the nest. She should be taken off at the same time each day for between ten and fifteen minutes. On no account must the eggs be allowed to get cool. Care must be taken when removing or replacing the broody on the nest to prevent damage to the eggs.

When the broody has obviously settled on the dummy eggs and has become quiet to handle, then these should be replaced with the clutch.

Normally, sufficient humidity will be provided from damp soil, although occasional damping may be advisable during the second and third week of incubation. If the weather is very dry, extra humidity may be needed, and this is best done by wetting the soil. Sprinkling the eggs with tepid water can be done in the later stages, but they must not be cooled excessively.

Once hatched, the chicks should be left for twenty-four hours to gain strength before being moved into a rearing coop. The broody is usually kept confined inside the coop while the young chicks are allowed access to a covered run. Food and water should be placed within reach of the foster mother and the chicks will soon learn to come when she calls them.

When the chicks are stronger, the run can be removed while the broody remains confined in the coop. They should be shut in at night with her.

The broody, poults and coop can be transported to the chosen site when it is time for release. Some protection may be necessary against foxes.

The young poults will quickly adapt to their surroundings and will soon become independent of their foster mother.

4.19 Bristol Incubator (PH 70) 700 pheasant eggs

4.20 Bristol Hatcher (PH 350) 3500 pheasant eggs

(Courtesy Patrick Pincker (Game Farm) Ltd.)

5
Rearing

Recommended Reading
Game Conservancy Advisory Booklets Nos. 8 and 18

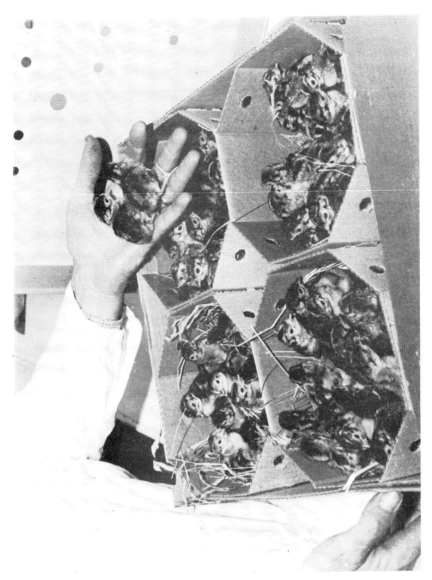

5.1 A 4-compartment chick box. Chicks will remain comfortably warm in these for several hours

(Courtesy Hardwick Game Farm, Suffolk

Rearing

Pheasants - General Information

The basic requirements of any newly hatched chick are food, water, heat and enough light to be able to see what it is doing. The most important of these in the first instance is heat, for young chicks very quickly become chilled and die.

PREPARATION OF BROODER

Rearing facilities should be overhauled and prepared well in advance. Whatever type of heater is used, it should be lit or switched on several hours before the chicks are put out and adjusted to give a temperature of about 100 degrees F (37.8 degrees C) immediately beneath it. A circular nursery area should be made; hardboard is useful for this purpose, to prevent the chicks from getting away from the brooder. Sufficient space must be left for the provision of food and water, and of course room for the chicks. Bedding should be of pea gravel or wood shavings, or better still, corrugated paper for the first few days, which eliminates the risk of the chicks eating the bedding. Hessian is sometimes used. Smooth surfaces must be avoided.

The food should be good quality high protein crumbs and should be placed in shallow pans. The lids of chick boxes or egg trays may be useful for this purpose. Water should be available and must also be shallow. If drinking fountains are used, stones should be placed in the bottom, or more conveniently, a length of hose pipe pushed into the water so that it is impossible for the little chicks to drown. Some keepers add a vitamin mix or an antibiotic mix to the water for the first five days, to give the chicks a good start.

There must be sufficient light to encourage activity.

5.2 Day old chicks, left to right: Pheasant, French partridge, English partridge

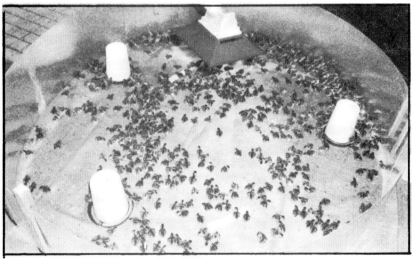

5.3 Partridge and pheasant chicks can be started off on hessian. The food can be sprinkled over the floor

INITIAL CARE 1-4 weeks

The chicks should be checked frequently at first. If there are signs of them huddling together under the heater, they are too cold and the temperature must be raised. If they are laid around the edge of the circle and not under the brooder at all, then they are too hot and the temperature must be lowered. If there is no heat control on the heater, the height of it should be adjusted.

During the first week a few deaths will occur naturally, especially around the fifth day. Until this age the yolk sac inside the chick is still being absorbed and is sufficient to keep the chick alive. If, however, it has not fed, then it dies when the yolk sac is gone. If losses are heavy or continue, and the chicks are not growing quickly and evenly, then disease must be suspected and arrangements made for post mortems to be carried out immediately to identify the causes.

As the chicks grow and become increasingly active, they must be given more space. If reared on grass, a very small area can be made available outside as early as three days if the weather conditions permit. Once again, a careful watch must be kept as young chicks very quickly become chilled. Whatever changes are made, they should be done gradually. At all times, wet areas should be cleaned up and stale food removed.

VICES

During the second week, more room should be provided. Feather pecking may begin to develop and should be remedied by de- beaking. Small plastic bits are also available for using on young chicks. Sometimes black chicks are set on by others, usually starting on the white feathers that develop on the wings. If there is any quantity of black or coloured chicks, it is advisable to put them all together in the same brooder. If they are attacked, then that particular pen can be dealt with as quickly as possible. Vent pecking must be stopped as soon as it occurs. This vice spreads rapidly with any age of chick or poult, and the victims seldom recover.

Keepers involved in a heavy rearing programme usually arrange to de-beak young pheasants at ten days of age. This fits in with the other weekly chores of setting and hatching eggs. Undue stress should be avoided as this may trigger off an outbreak of disease. The chicks should continue to be shut in the brooder huts at night.

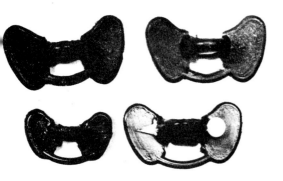

Full wing birds can now be fitted with spex without the risk of hanging themselves on aviary nets. Built in pins allow quick fixing and less discomfort to the bird.

DE-BEAKING

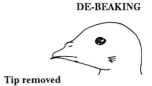

Tip removed

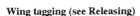

Wing tagging (see Releasing)

Position of wing tag
to allow for growth

Poult put in hole cut in top of box

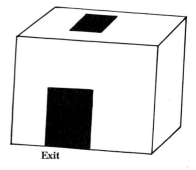

Simple handling device
to prevent chicks or poults
becoming mixed again
after handling

Exit

Exit hole put against pophole into hut, shelter pen or grass run

AIDS TO MANAGEMENT

FURTHER DEVELOPMENT

During the third week the chicks will be feathering up. They should be allowed full access to the rearing area by three weeks of age. A small mini pellet should be gradually introduced into the diet, and a small amount of flint grit provided to aid digestion. A continued watch must be kept for signs of feather pecking because a young pheasant's beak soon grows again after de-beaking. Feather pecking at this age usually begins on the back and is often difficult to detect unless a bird is caught and closely examined. Any symptoms of ill health should be noted and quickly diagnosed. Coccidiosis frequently occurs at around three weeks and the risk will be increased if the weather is wet.

During the fourth week, bitting or a further de-beaking is usually carried out either when necessary, or as a routine precaution. The stress caused by handling may trigger off disease, so continual care is needed.

HARDENING OFF

Weather permitting, the heater can be turned off during the day. It should be continued to be lit or switched on at night, though, if it is warm enough, some or all the poults need not be shut in at night. If there is a thermostat on the heater, this can be lowered. Pheasants that are too cold will smother each other in an effort to keep warm. Excessive heat may also cause smothering when an attempt is made to get away from it. Common sense must be used with regard to provision of heat. There is no sense in attempting to harden off the poults at an early age, and to lose several in the process.

CARE OF THE POULT 4-7 weeks

Between the fourth and the sixth week, the mini pellet should be replaced by a larger growers or rearers pellet. This will be of a lower protein value than the chick crumbs and the mini pellet. The really high protein rations are only necessary during the first few weeks. A continued watch must be kept for further outbreaks of feather pecking and another de-beaking may be necessary. The poults can be left outside at night unless wet weather is forecast.

When the poults are too large to be caught easily in one hand, they must be handled with care. Legs or wings are very easily broken and feathers pulled out. Poults will quickly die if smothered in a corner when they panic.

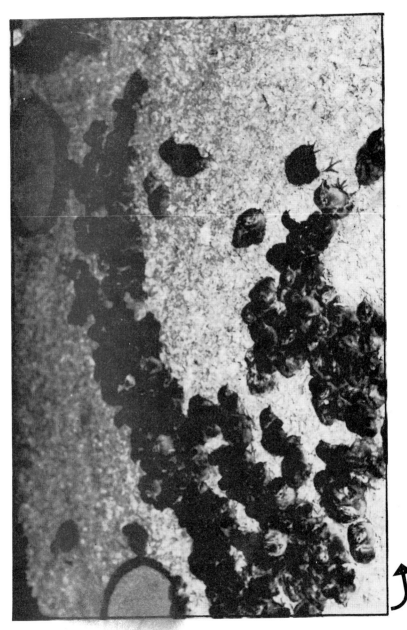

5.4 Young chicks should not be huddled under the heater nor laid around the outside edge of the nursery area. Ideally there should be an area immediately beneath the heater unoccupied. This allows for the chicks to obtain extra warmth should it be needed

5.5 A large scale rearing enterprise

(Courtey Mr. M. Wingrove)

5.6 Conventional rearing system

5.7 A 500-chick size Hardwick gas brooder and a well designed shelter pen

(Courtesy Hardwick Game Farm, Suffolk)

5.8 Large circular brooder unit ideal for rearing a large number of pheasant or partridge chicks

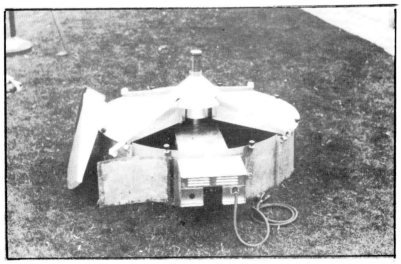

5.9 Rupert type brooder dismantled to show interior gas heating element

(Courtesy Hardwick Game Farm, Suffolk)

Releasing usually takes place when the poults are at least six weeks old, by which time they should be off heat completely. If coccidiosis has been prevalent, a precautionary dose of medicine should be given prior to the birds leaving the rearing field.

RELEASING

The release pen should have been prepared and checked immediately before the poults are put in.

Ideally the pheasants should be moved no later than mid- afternoon, so that they have time to settle before night-fall. If at all possible, they should not be moved when it is raining or heavy rain is forecast.

Poults are best transported in crates and an extra helper or two will greatly speed up the operation.

All bits must be removed from their beaks. Whether they are wing clipped is purely a matter of the individual choice. There are advantages and disadvantages. If it is decided to do so, then only the outer half dozen feathers should be cut. Adult primary feathers will already be developing near the centre of the wing and these must not be clipped on any account. If the poult is more than seven weeks old, the wing feathers should be pulled out instead of cut, as the adult feathers will be even more developed. They will soon grow again.

Wing tagging, if required, is most easily done before the poults are crated. These should be fixed in the loose skin at the front of the wing and allowance must be made for growth. Special pliers are required to secure most types of tags. A new design of wing tag has very recently been marketed which can be inserted with a 'gun;. This has been developed from the method used by manufacturers to securely fix labels, etc. to their goods. Tagging is expensive and makes work both when the tags are put in and when they are searched for at the end of a shoot day. They are useful for establishing a pattern of movement or for identifying birds that are not suitable for breeding from the following year. Alternatively, leg rings can be fitted. This is also time consuming, but identification is obvious at a short distance and they are much more easily seen on shot game.

Feed

It is preferable to use rations specially manufactured for game birds. These are formulated to contain all the necessary vitamins, minerals, oil, fibre and protein that are required by game birds during their different stages of growth. If other rations have to be used, then turkey food is the most suitable

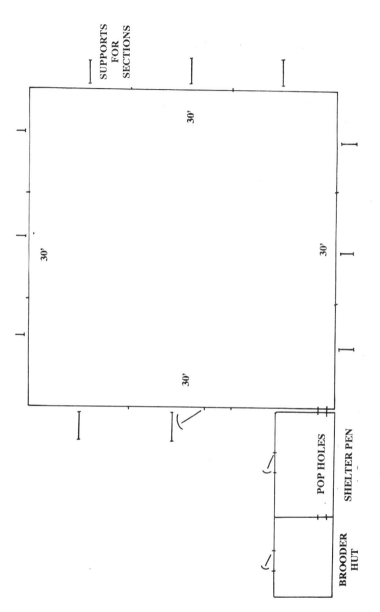

SUPPORTS FOR SECTIONS

30'

30'

30'

30'

POP HOLES

SHELTER PEN

BROODER HUT

The shelter pen must be roofed and the sides preferably covered with reinforced polythene. The grass run is constructed from wire netting 10' x 5' sections. 12 will be needed, vis 10 plain, 1 with agate and 1 with a pop hole

DIAGRAM OF TYPICAL REARING UNIT FOR 250 POULTS

5.10 *The automatic drinker illustrated is cheap, efficient and suitable for young chicks*

5.11 *The base of tube feeders can be used for young chicks*

5.12 Interior of brooder house showing heater, drinkers, feed pans and hardboard surround

5.13 Ducks are easy to rear but exceedingly messy in their habits

(Courtesy Hardwick Game Farm, Suffolk)

5.14 40 gallon container converted into a feed hopper using a device to prevent wastage and to keep the food dry

(Courtesy Hardwick Game Farm, Suffolk)

5.15 'Gaybird' type gas heater

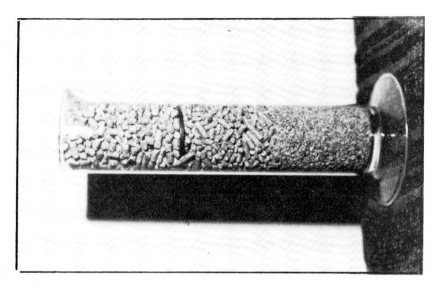

5.16 Good quality feed must be used. 3 grades are manufactured. Crumbs (bottom), mini pellet (middle) and rearers or growers pellets (top)

5.17 This larger size automatic drinker is free-standing and can be used for older poults on the rearing field or in the release pen

substitute. Whenever poultry rations are used as a replacement, attention must be paid to any warnings issued on the label attached to every bag.

Drugs that are toxic to game birds are included in some poultry rations.

Many game bird feed compounds incorporate drugs at a preventative level. The letters A.C.S. denote that a coccidiostat is included and the letters A.B.H. that an anti-blackhead drug is incorporated. On request, Mebenvet, at a curative level for gapes, is available from most manufacturers.

Individual firms use their own formula to produce game food and, although compounds vary slightly, on average they are as follows:

FOOD	PROTEIN	OIL	FIBRE
Breeder Pellet	17%	3%	4.5%
Chick Crumbs	28%	3.5%	3.5%
Rearing Mini Pellet	25%	3.2%	3.5%
Growers Pellet	20%	3.0%	4.25%
Poult or Covert Pellet	15%	2.0%	5.5%

During the first few days after hatching, the food should be placed in shallow pans or on egg trays that are placed where chicks can easily find them. If corrugated paper is used on the floor, it is a good idea to sprinkle some crumbs over the whole area.

Once the chicks are feeding properly, other types of feeders can be introduced that will prevent the wastage that occurs with open feeders. Tube feeders, as for poultry, are ideal as they will only require topping up once a day and provide a constant supply of clean food. Adjustment can be made to eliminate wastage. The tops should be kept covered to prevent fouling and to prevent young birds from falling in and being unable to get out again.

Flat troughs with either a roller bar or a lid are equally suitable, but care must be taken that there is no part of the feeder where a chick or poult may get its head stuck or leg trapped. Ample feed space must be provided.

Later on, feed hoppers can be made from old five gallon drums or even forty gallon containers. Devices are manufactured that can be fitted into a suitable container that will prevent wastage, access by smaller birds and will stop the food inside becoming wet.

Hoppers should be introduced to poults on the rearing field if it is intended to use them in release pens.

It is very important to store food in dry conditions, as it will soon become musty and mouldy where it is damp. Bags should never be placed directly onto a brick or concrete floor, but should be stacked on pallets or a layer of polythene.

Rations should not be stored for long periods, as they will deteriorate. A date is usually printed on the label by which time the food should be used.

Water

Availability of water is important at all times and vices such as feather pecking may occur if birds are allowed to become thirsty. Water should be available to newly hatched chicks in containers that are not too deep that they may drown. Either shallow pans may be used, or glass, plastic or galvanised fountains. To start with, stones or, better still, a length of pipe should be placed around the base. A day old chick can easily drown in an inch of water and it is as well to keep the water shallow for at least a week.

All drinkers must be kept clean and the area around them kept dry. Wet shavings and droppings must not be allowed to build up, as this increases the risk of disease. It is important to ensure that the drinker is level, to prevent seepage. Fresh water should be provided at least once every day, and drinkers should not be placed in a position too near to the heater, as the water inside may become too hot for the chicks to drink.

Medication is most frequently given via the drinking water. Instructions for usage and rate of dosage must be carefully followed. As it is almost always necessary to mix it up fresh each day, an estimation should be made of the amount likely to be consumed in that period to avoid wastage.

When drugs are used in the water, any medication incorporated in the food must be taken into consideration when working out the dosage.

Consumption of water will be increased during hot weather and an adequate number of drinkers must be provided.

Automatic drinkers are a useful and labour-saving item of equipment. It is wisest to use them only in grass runs where poults are reared out of doors. A disaster can occur if a drinker overflows inside a brooder hut at night.

Care must also be taken if used as part of an intensive system indoors. Automatic drinkers are not infallible, and flooding is always a risk. Medication of individual units can also be a problem.

Water can be transported to the rearing field in farm-discarded five gallon containers. Alternatively, a specially designed tanker can be pulled by a vehicle. Strategically placed tanks or old baths can be filled, and buckets of water are quickly filled from them. Occasionally, it is possible to lay mains water to the rearing field with alkathene piping.

Housing and Heaters

Pheasants, partridges and duck can be reared virtually anywhere, providing that conditions are dry, draught proof and precautions are taken to prevent the chicks or poults escaping. Pheasants and partridges can fly well at an early age., so all outdoor pens need to be covered with a net. Buildings used for intensive rearing will need small mesh wire fixed over windows, eaves, etc. Small holes beneath doors and in walls or partitions will need filling.

To start with, chicks will need to be confined within a circle beneath the brooder. Sufficient room must be provided for them not to be overheated and for the provision of food and water. Two foot (60 cms.) high lengths of hardboard or tin are suitable to form a nursery area and can be held together by pegs made from off-cuts of wood.

This area should be extended as the chicks grow. A two foot (60 cms.) high surround will generally confine chicks for the first ten days, after which time their wing feathers are sufficiently developed for them to fly over.

There must be ample light to begin with, so that chicks will feed. Later on, when birds are reared intensively, it is beneficial to darken the building to prevent feather pecking.

There are many types of heaters that can be used to rear game birds. Some are more suitable than others, for a variety of reasons.

Paraffin is little used, although the **Rupert Type Brooder** (see Figs. 5.17/18) is still popular for rearing small numbers. A Rupert type brooder is a circular low brooder made from galvanised steel or, more recently, different manufacturers have used fibreglass. Warm air is ducted around the interior from a burner set in the back. The chicks have access in and out through a curtain at the front. Rupert brooders provide as similar conditions as possible to natural brooding by a hen.

There is sometimes difficulty with paraffin models in maintaining the correct temperature. It is also advisable to use them in conjunction with a shelter pen.

Propane gas models or conversions are now available, as are brooders with a capacity of up to 500 pheasant chicks.

Chicks must not be left shut inside of Rupert type brooders if the sun is shining on them. The temperature inside will soon rise to an uncomfortable level in the sunshine. Also, chicks are only shut inside at night for the first few days.

5.18 Original paraffin model Rupert Brooder designed to hold 100 pheasant chicks

5.19 English partridge chicks in a Rupert Brooder. Note small nursery area, hose pipe in base of drinker and large, shallow feed pan

Electric Brooders

Many different types of electric heaters are available. There are several disadvantages to using electricity, but the one main advantage is its convenience.

The disadvantages are:

a) Sitings of rearing units are dependent on the availability of power points.

b) The risk of power cuts. Thunderstorms often occur during rearing time and increase this risk.

c) Some electric heaters emit light as well as heat, e.g. infra red lamps, and feather pecking may develop as a direct result.

Electric heaters designed for game can be divided into two categories: heat provided from above, and heat provided by contact.

Generally, the most popular electric heater is the **Electric Hen**. Two sizes are available which will take either 125 or 250 pheasant chicks. The top of the brooder is filled with shavings or similar substance and covered. The legs are adjusted so that the chicks can comfortably walk beneath, where they come into contact with the base. Heat is provided by an element similar to an electric blanket. Some keepers prefer this method of rearing, but there are some disadvantages. The brooders get very dirty and require some time spent on cleaning when finished with. Care must be taken that the base covering does not get damaged or torn. There is no heat adjustment, other than altering the height, so it is sometimes necessary to make sure that the building does not get too cold. If the chicks are not warm enough, they will be noted scrumming beneath the centre of the brooder.

A further disadvantage is that it is not possible to see what is happening beneath without lifting the brooder up and disturbing the chicks.

The other types of heater include infra red lamps, dull emitters and radiant bar. Large canopy models with thermostats fitted are available for rearing large numbers.

Gas Brooders

The most popular method of rearing game birds on grass is propane gas. This is available in full (47 kgs.) or half size cylinders and can be sited almost anywhere.

There are several sizes of heater available. The smallest is suitable for use in a conventional outdoor rearing system for 125 pheasant chicks using a four foot by four foot brooder house. When the weather is mild, this will be adequate in a slightly larger house, but does not emit enough heat to be suitable at the beginning of the rearing season when the nights are often cold. Larger heaters are manufactured to provide sufficient heat for 250 or 500 chicks. Large canopy models can be purchased for rearing intensively on gas delivered in bulk and stored in a tank.

The smallest size **Gay Bird** type heater has no adjustment for heat output and, under normal conditions, a large cylinder of gas is sufficient to meet the requirements of a batch of birds. The larger models, which often have some form of heat control, will obviously use a larger quantity of gas. Temperature controls are operated by three methods; a thermostat, a manually operated control on the heater, or more conveniently, a manually adjusted control on the regulator outside the hut. This allows for the alterations to be made without disturbing the chicks.

The normal arrangement is for the gas cylinder to be stood outside the house and the hose connecting the heater to be threaded through a ventilation hole in the back or front of the brooder house. A regulator is required to connect the hose to the cylinder. The heater should be suspended on a chain or wire from the roof of the hut.

There are several disadvantages with using gas.

Firstly, there is no visible means of knowing the amount of gas remaining in the cylinder, so that there is always the risk of the heater going out overnight. The weight of the cylinder is a rough guide and, occasionally, weather conditions will cause condensation to form where the gas is inside. This risk of gas running out can be overcome by purchasing either a device that will indicate the volume of gas remaining, or a changeover valve that will link the part-used bottle with a full one. Both these items are expensive.

The initial expense of purchasing heaters, hoses and regulators is another disadvantage to using gas, although the running costs compare favourably with electricity. Electric hens are probably the cheapest form of heater, and infra red or dull emitter the most costly to use. There is very little work needed for the maintenance of gas heaters, other than an occasional blowing through to keep the jet clear and remove dust. Air filters, where fixed, will need to be kept clear of dust and, after use, the hose and canopy will require washing.

One thing that must be remembered, when using gas, is the risk of fire. The heater should never be hung from a rope or string. Chain or wire should always be used. If more than one heater is used in a building, then they must all be fitted with a flame failure device which automatically shuts off the supply of gas should the burner go out for any reason.

5.20 Existing buildings can be adapted to provide a semi-intensive rearing system

(Courtesy Hardwick Game Farm, Suffolk)

If one of these devices is not fitted to a heater, and it has gone out, the supply of gas must be turned off and the brooder house well ventilated before any attempt is made to re-light the brooder. It is exceedingly dangerous to strike a match where gas has built up in an enclosed area.

LAYOUT OF OUTDOOR BROODER UNIT

A system used for rearing 250 pheasant poults usually comprises of a brooder hut 8 ft x 60 ft, a covered shelter pen 10 ft x 6 ft and an outside pen either 30 ft x 30 ft or 40 ft x 20 ft, covered with a net. See diagram. The latter size pen (40 ft x 20 ft) makes it easier for the poults to be driven into the shelter pen by one person. The square pen often requires the help of an assistant. Wire ties (as used for doing up bags of potatoes) are ideal for joining sections together and can be fastened very tightly using a special tool. The ground where the unit is sited should be level and any holes beneath the sections should be carefully blocked. If the soil is well drained, it is not necessary to have floors in the huts. Where the ground is liable to become waterlogged, then it is advisable to have floors. As an added precaution, it may be necessary to dig a channel around the hut and particularly at the back to drain water away from off the roof.

The basic requirements for an outdoor rearing system are initially expensive.

A brooder house, shelter pen, outside run, feeders, drinkers, heater, supports for the sections, a net and two props to hold it up, are all needed.Compared with the possibility of utilising existing farm buildings, the cost can seem prohibitive. The main benefit with outdoor rearing is the quality of poult produced. A sleek, well feathered bird that is acclimatised to rain and cooler temperatures will stand a far greater chance of survival in the release pen than a dry, dusty indoor reared poult.

If it is practical to use buildings where the poults can run outside, then it is possible to produce quality poults on a semi- intensive system. Where this is done, the permanent outside areas should be limed and sprayed with a suitable disinfectant to eliminate a buildup of disease.

Rearing Partridges

Very much the same principles apply to rearing partridges as to the pheasant. Special partridge rations are formulated, but they will thrive just as well on most pheasant rations if necessary.

Partridges are not so prone to feather pecking as pheasants, so it may not be necessary to de-beak or bit them. This, however, should be done if an outbreak occurs. Young partridges often peck at each other's toes or nostrils and losses may be sustained. It is advisable to de-beak should this happen.

The hybrid French partridges are easy to rear, provided they can be kept healthy; the pure French a little more difficult, and the English are more troublesome. Most problems occur from the birds being highly strung and becoming easily stressed. Occasionally, partridge chicks develop the habit of eating wood shavings, twigs and dry grass stems, etc., that prove indigestible and cause death through impaction of the gizzard. There is no known reason for this and no prevention other than denying them the opportunity.

Problems may also be encountered when the poults are older and something triggers off a full scale panic. French partridges, as well as English, are prone to this behaviour and, for no apparent reason, will suddenly run or fly blindly around the pen. Sometimes injury or death occurs as they hit the wire netting or nets. There seems no obvious reason or way of preventing this from happening.

Duck

Mallard are very easy to rear, but are exceedingly messy in their habits. When first hatched, they are just as liable to drown in the drinkers as pheasants, so shallow pans must be provided. Virtually any type of heater may be used and their only vice may be fluff pulling, usually caused by overcrowding. Due to the shape of their beaks, they are neither de-beaked or bitted.

Ducklings will eat almost anything in great quantities. They should be started off on crumbs and then pellets which can be later replaced with meal if it is more convenient. At a later stage, barley can be fed instead of wheat.

It is important that eggs or ducklings should be selected only from stock that is known to fly well.

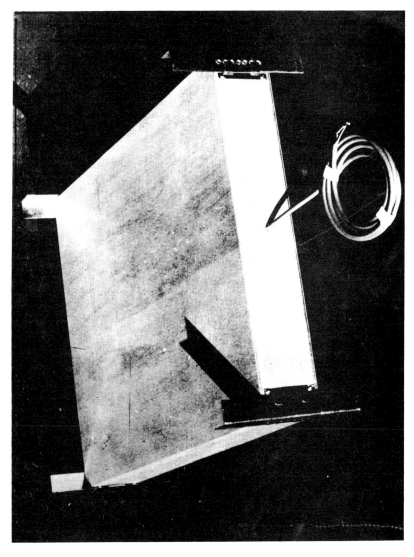

5.21 Bristol Eectric Hen (100-200 chicks) Brooder

(Courtesy Patrick Pincher (Game Farm) Ltd.)

6

Releasing Birds

Recommended reading

Game Conservancy Advisory Booklets
Numbers 4, 8, 9, 14 & 18

Releasing Pheasants

The siting and construction of a release pen is dealt with in Chapter 5.

Immediately prior to release, the pen should be inspected. Previously, feed tracks should have been cut, the electric fence (if used) trimmed out and checked that it is working, and drinkers should have been cleaned and filled.

The poults or ex-laying stock should be transported and released in the pen before mid-afternoon, allowing them time to find their way about and to settle down. Any escapees should be walked quietly back in through the re-entry tunnels.

CRATES

The best designed crates for transporting pheasants are ones with a side opening, as well as a top opening, and solid floors. The crates can then be placed near some cover, the side opened, and the pheasants allowed to walk quietly out. If it is necessary to take them out of the top of the crate, this should be done also in cover so that they are less likely to attempt to fly. This is especially important if the wings have not been clipped.

MANAGEMENT

It is unwise to mix poults of more than one week's difference in age. The older ones will bully the younger ones. If it is unavoidable that ages have to be mixed, it is wisest to put all the poults in the pen as near the same time as possible.

The pen should not be over-crowded. A minimum perimeter size of one yard per bird is recommended, although this may be somewhat decreased over 250.

FEEDING

The poults must be given plenty of food and drinkers in all parts of the pen. This is particularly important in a large pen where poults may at first get lost. It is a good policy to feed right up to the perimeter fence in several places, as the young birds may well follow the fence round. When a very large pen is used, some keepers prefer to build a smaller one inside where the poults can

6.1 Automatic feeders are manufactured that run off 12v battery. They are
fitted with a time switch and a calling device

be kept for a day or two to get acclimatised before being let into the larger pen.

Once the poults are settled down, the feed can be slightly cut back so that they are getting hungry by feed times. Generally, pheasants are fed twice a day, although some keepers feed three times. At this stage the poults should be accustomed to the whistle or other call. If feeders have been brought from the rearing field to use while the poults are getting used to being fed on the ground, these should be removed. Feed hoppers can be introduced if it is intended to use them after release.

POSSIBLE PROBLEMS

After two or three weeks, problems are likely to occur. Feather pecking may develop and, to help this, straw should be spread along the feed rides to keep the poults otherwise occupied. The ground cover will mostly have been eaten and a few branches can be bent down to provide some greenery. Feather pecking may also be a sign that the poults are suffering from disease and a careful watch must be kept. Gapes is most likely at this time, especially after wet weather, and a severe outbreak must be treated. Tail corn or cleanings tipped in the release pens will also help to keep the poults occupied.

As time passes, the poults will grow stronger and their juvenile wing feathers will be replaced with adult feathers. They will begin to fly out of the pen, particularly as they come off roost in the mornings. If foxes or other vermin are prevalent, every attempt should be made to drive the poults back inside the pen at night, where they will be safe. It is very important to test the electric fence is working at all times.

The benefit of training the pheasants to connect the whistle or other sound with being fed will become obvious once the birds get out of the pen. After a while, it will no longer be practical to attempt to get them back inside, so a feed ride should be made outside the pen. By now, wheat should be introduced as part of the diet.

Standing crops or loose straw in the vicinity of the release area may induce the pheasants to juk on the ground instead of going to roost; a habit which may prove fatal should a fox discover them. At all times, vermin control is important when birds are both inside and outside of the pen. Corn where pheasants juk should not be combined at night as, stupid birds that pheasants are, they will not move out of the way.

As harvest progresses, open fields and stubbles will cause pheasants to stray. Blackberries, spilled corn and other seeds, will provide sufficient food that they are not obliged to return to the pen. Much of a keeper's time may

6.2 Feed hoppers can be cheaply made from discarded 5 gallon drums. Hopper feeding is only successful when there are adequate hoppers, as frequently one cock bird will dominate a feeder

6.3 This implement will transport a ton of wheat and dispense into bins when towed by a tractor. A useful tool on a large shoot

be spent in driving or dogging them in away from the boundaries of other undesirable areas. Only the release area will be fed and the addition of some whole or kibbled maize may prove attractive.

When the decision is made to release all the pheasants, the wire should be fastened up in as many places as possible to allow free access.

Acorns and beech masts will continue to entice pheasants away after harvest, and may prove a problem in a year when they are plentiful.

FEEDING OUT

The feeding of outlying coverts and game crops usually begins in mid- or late-September. In some areas where stubbles are left, or other food is available, it may be December before the pheasants begin to appear on these feed rides.

Feeding is the only control a keeper has over the movements of his pheasants and is very important in producing results. A balance needs to be kept between allowing the birds to become too hungry (and looking elsewhere for food), and not feeding them so much that they do not bother to appear. Corn sprouting green on a feed ride is a sign of bad keepering and wasteful feeding.

A skilful keeper can manipulate his pheasants to be where he wants them at a certain time when he wants them there. This is obviously more difficult in a year when there is an abundance of natural food. It is also very difficult to achieve if hopper feeding *ad lib* is practised. Outlying coverts are generally fed once a day, but twice daily feeding continues at release sites until after they have been shot.

From October onwards, extra watch must be kept for poachers. Many keepers even find it necessary these days to have an alarm or security system fitted to their release pens or even the rearing field.

Birds should be discouraged from roosting near public roads or near boundaries, and it is as well to avoid feed rides that are in public view. Some keepers have the conviction that feeding their boundaries will entice a few of their neighbours' pheasants onto their shoot. In actual fact, it is more than likely to draw their own birds out to the boundaries.

The national average returns of birds shot to that of birds released is approximately 40%.

Feeding should continue right through the winter until the end of March. It is particularly important after the shooting season because this is the

6.4 Poults must be healthy and well feathered when leaving the rearing field. Bits must be removed.

6.5 Straw can be provided to keep pheasant poults occupied in the release pen.

hungriest time of the year. If pheasants are to be in peak condition for breeding, they must be well fed.

RELEASING PARTRIDGE

Releasing partridges involves a different technique to that of releasing pheasants. The difficulty arises with trying to keep the partridges in small numbered groups. They normally live in family groups called a covey. The tendency is for reared partridges, when released, to form one very large covey. When the time comes to drive them, this very large covey will rise in the air all at the same time and fly over the guns together. The system of release devised is designed to prevent this from happening, but it does not always succeed.

Partridges are not usually released until they are at least ten weeks old. By this time the majority of the harvest will be complete and straw burning finished. If the partridges have been bitted, these must be removed. The wings are neither clipped nor pulled. Wing tagging or leg ringing can be done if required.

Small covered sectional pens are erected in secluded and sheltered positions. They should be as far apart as possible, but within the intended drive.

Each pen should be furnished with a feed hopper, a drinker and a straw bale inside and outside.

Between 15 and 30 partridges, either English or French, should be placed inside and allowed to settle for a day or two. After this, two or three birds should be allowed to walk quietly out of the pen each day until only three or four remain. These should be retained in the pen to act as an anchor for those released. If there are many French partridges to be released, the first covey can be fully released and a fresh lot put in the pen the same day that the last few are let out. This second lot will act as an anchor for the rest and, very often, will stay separate from the original group when released.

POSSIBLE PROBLEMS

In theory, this system should work well. Food and water is available for birds released, and the straw bales are placed so that the partridges can stand on them, see each other, and call to each other. In practice, problems do arise. Coveys of released partridges sometimes wander great distances and may require driving in. A dog is useless for this as French partridges, particularly, are reluctant to fly and merely run away from a dog. They are usually unwilling to cross open fields and often the only solution is to walk them

6.6 French partridge released in maize.

6.7 Regular feeding is important. Pheasants, French and English partridges waiting for their rations on a January morning.

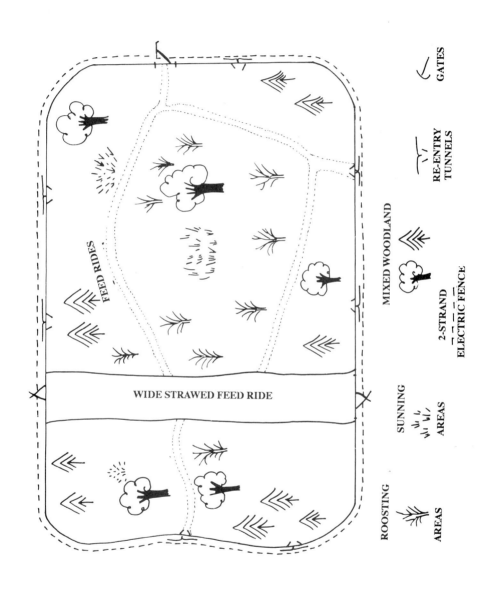

DIAGRAM OF LAYOUT OF LARGE RELEASE PEN

steadily back along hedgerows, fence lines or tracks until they are returned to the release site. Once released, much time may be spent driving around in search of errant coveys.

Added to this problem is that the food at release sites also attracts pheasants and often this source of food is in an area where it is not wished to draw pheasants. This problem can be overcome by covering the food hopper with large mesh wire netting or weld mesh which will allow partridges entry, but deny access to pheasants.

Releasing partridges has its problems, but even so, returns for French partridges can be on a par with that of pheasants. Taking into account that they are easier and cheaper to rear, and provide some earlier and varied sport, they are gaining in popularity.

A few keepers release large quantities of French partridges successfully in a similar way to pheasants, i.e. in a large communal pen.

Alternative method of releasing English partridge

The returns for English partridge are a lot lower than that of French or pheasants.

An alternative method of releasing English partridges is successful if there are sufficient pairs of barren adults on the estate.

Small pens are placed in the territory of a known barren pair. Between 12 and 20 young poults are put inside and a watch kept on them. In most cases the barren pair will come to the young ones. When this adoption has obviously taken place, the young should be released and the pen removed immediately.

All partridges should be released at least a month before shooting, to allow them to become wild, gain strength and to be familiar with the ground. They should be at least fourteen weeks old before shooting commences. Feeding needs to be continued *ad lib.*

Duck releasing

Duck should not be released until they are fully feathered, i.e. approximately seven weeks. They should be put on a pond of sufficient size that they are safe from predators. If possible, the pond should not be too near pheasant release pens as ducks are greedy and will soon discover the feed ride.

Ducks, because of their bodily shape, are easiest to carry by the neck when they are caught up.

After release, they should be fed around the edge of the pond. If adjoining a field of standing corn, they may flatten areas where they feed on it.

6.8 Mallard ducks will become very tame.

Other than the necessary visits to feed, it is well to keep away. Mallard become very tame if encouraged, and difficulty may arise when a shoot is arranged and they are reluctant to fly. Some keepers feed them away from the pond so that they learn to fly to and fro.

The opposite problem is sometimes encountered. On a shoot day the duck are driven off the pond over waiting guns. Instead of circling around at a shootable height, they can be seen rising higher and higher until they are well out of range.

In recent years, rearing duck has lost favour and French partridge has filled the niche once occupied by the duck. Some are still reared to supplement shoots and to recompense for wild duck shot.

Overall, duck are often regarded as disease carriers. They are expensive to rear, consuming vast quantities of food, and their flying ability is often either lacking or exceeding requirements.

The ban that may be legally imposed on shooting wildfowl during a spell of severe weather also applies to reared duck.

6.9 Pheasant poult crate with top and side openings

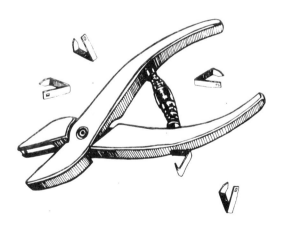

6.10 Wing tags and pliers

(Courtesy Patrick Pincker (Game Farm) Ltd.)

6.11 Pheasant poults will fly when let out of a crate

7
Woodland release pens and cover crops

Recommended reading

Game Conservancy Booklets
Numbers 2 and 15

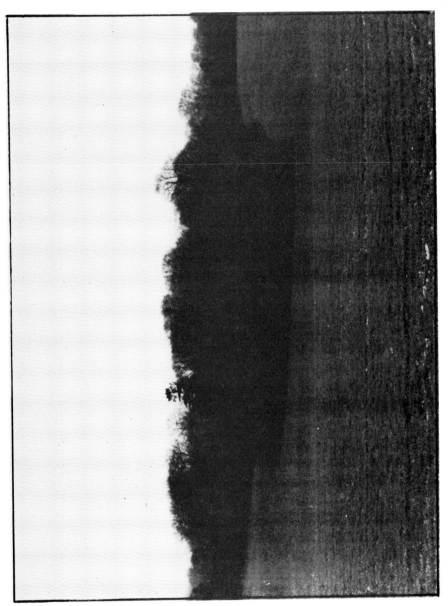

7.1 Woods originally planted for shooting provide a suitable area to head a drive, often planted with shrubs

The Woods

On most shoots it is the woodland that has been most neglected during the past. Coppicing was once a part of woodland management. Areas were cut on rotation, which meant that there was a selection of different stages of growth. This suited game management, as it supplied a varied habitat. During the last war, many hundreds of acres of timber were felled and replaced with plantations of soft woods.

CONIFER PLANTATIONS

These fir trees are not so beneficial as hardwoods, although they are attractive at certain stages of growth.

When first planted the weeds growing amongst the evenly spaced trees attract pheasants. After a few years, the undergrowth begins to prevail; birch and bramble grow profusely. As time goes on, the trees grow taller and the light is obliterated from beneath. The undergrowth dies off without sufficient light, and the plantations grow into dark forests devoid of ground cover. Hen pheasants show a preference for fir plantations.

Vast areas of conifer woods make shoot management difficult.

Narrow rides are adequate for feeding, vermin control and handling beaters, but wider and more open areas are needed for release sites and for placing the guns.

During the first year or two after planting, a block will be attractive to game and be easily managed. But when the trees reach head height and the rubbish growth is dense, problems arise. Tracks will need to be cut for the beaters to penetrate. The pheasants will tend to fly badly, preferring to skim the tops of the trees rather than to gain height. At a later stage the trees are brashed (the low branches cut off) and this cover left lying between the rows of trees may make it very difficult to evict the birds. As the fir trees grow rapidly taller, the light will become obliterated and the ground cover die off.

7.2 A useful wood with game cover grown beside.

This is of manageable size, situated on high ground and with a good hedge below that is suitable for driving either pheasants or partridges over.

7.3 Woods that are kept sheltered by shrubs grown round the perimeter are preferred by pheasants

The woods will be dark and bare and not hospitable to pheasants during the day time, although they may choose to roost in them at night.

IDEAL HABITAT

The ideal woodland for pheasants should be a mixture of hard and soft woods. It should contain clearings and wide rides, a variety of vegetation with shrubs or conifers planted around the edges to provide shelter and warmth. The wood should be of manageable size, have suitable flushing points, and not be on an exposed site. Coverts meeting these requirements are very rare, as most have been neglected over the years. However, a few improvements can be made by the keeper that incur very little expense and will prove beneficial for holding birds.

Timber for firewood is always in demand and cutting can often be arranged in areas that suit the shoot organisation. In this way, small areas can be cleared that will provide nesting cover or undergrowth at flushing points. The ground vegetation quickly regenerates when trees and bushes have been cleared. The income from the sale of firewood can be ploughed back and used to purchase shrubs, such as Lonicera, that can be planted for shelter or from which to flush pheasants. Hard woods, too, can be purchased for planting small areas of uncultivatable land. Grants are sometimes available for these. Young trees of three years of age are called 'whips', and these are ideal for such purposes. These soon become established and the use of plastic protective sleeves eliminates the costly outlay for wire netting which, in itself, is a hazard that has to be taken into account when planning a drive. Shrubs such as rhododendron should be avoided as they may grow quickly and become inpenetrable.

If a chainsaw is available for the keeper's use, overhanging branches can be cleared from rides and small sections inside of release pens cut back to provide areas that will prove attractive to pheasants.

On a sporting estate the woods can be compared with the heart, and the hedges surrounding it likened to the arteries. The heart provides roosting, shelter, nesting cover and food in the form of acorn or beech masts or wheat fed by the keeper.

The hedges are the highways and byeways for pheasants and vermin. Predator control is most efficient in hedgerows and pheasants prefer to follow hedge or fence lines to travel from one covert to another. Food, shelter from the wind and nesting cover are also provided by a hedge, the removal of which has a devastating effect on movement and the breeding success of game.

7.4 When roadways and headlands have been cleared, good pheasant and partridge drives can be had from fields of sugar beet.

7.5 Where a game crop has failed (in this case kale) fat hen may grow. This is particularly attractive to both pheasants and partridges and may still provide a useful drive.

Siting of game crops

Game crops can be planted at strategic places alongside hedgerows. These can greatly improve a shoot by making it possible to show and present pheasants in a better way than that achieved from woodland. If the sites are carefully chosen, the birds will often fly much better when driven back towards a wood than they would have from out of it.

Planting game crops is expensive, so forethought should be given to the size of strip, the positioning of it, and the choice of cover used. Good results may not be achieved if a block is planted in the middle of a field. There should preferably be a track or hedge linking the game cover with the woodland.

An experienced keeper should be able to draw his birds out into the cover from the wood. It is often good management to shoot the covers a few times before driving the wood, which will act as a reservoir.

Flushing point

In Woodland, if it is not possible to drive the pheasants to a natural point, then they need to be flushed amongst the trees. Attention must be paid to the heading chosen and improvements made where possible. Pheasants will be unable and unwilling to rise up through a thick canopy of leaves and branches. Therefore, a relatively clear area will be needed for them to gain height. A low cover of shrubs at the flushing point will help prevent them all rising together or running up to the sewelling or wire netting if it is used.

Sewelling is invaluable in large woods as a prevention for birds running on. It can be used along rides to prevent leakage from the sides of the drive and in the heading to rise birds where required. It should be jerked at intervals to prevent the pheasants ignoring it. Wire netting is sometimes used for a similar purpose, but birds in large numbers will gather against it and panic, often damaging themselves in the process or becoming exhausted.

Sewelling can also be used to rise birds fifty or so yards back from the edge of the cover so that they make better birds when they reach the guns.

Presenting quality birds

A pheasant only has a limited amount of energy to expend on gaining height. If this is spent struggling through branches, then it will drop down as soon as that energy has been used. By being aware of this fact, and rising birds in a clear area and placing the guns in a position where the pheasant has gained most height, the quality of shooting can be greatly improved. By utilising the

7.6 Mustard sown at the end of June will provide attractive cover for pheasants and partridges throughout the shooting season.

7.7 Stubble burning is a part of the modern agricultural system, but it is something the gamekeeper could well do without.

contours of the ground and taking into account the prevailing wind and other conditions, more testing shots can be presented.

Quality, rather than quantity, is most often appreciated, but a combination of the two should guarantee complete satisfaction. If the quantity of birds is available, then the individual shots can be selected to provide the quality if the birds are well presented.

As a general rule, pheasants will not fly well uphill and will fly much better if they have somewhere to fly to. Few pheasants will launch themselves towards an open space. The tendency for them, when presented with such a task, is to turn back over the wood or along the sides. All this should be taken into consideration when drives are planned. When a small day is required, covers can be driven back to the release site which is then left quiet. If a large day is planned, the drives should be designed so that the birds are driven over the guns more than once in a day. By driving covers towards one or two centre points, and then driving these centre points at a later stage during the day, all the birds on a beat will have been gathered together. Where this is done a beat should be left for at least two and preferably three weeks before it is shot again, to allow pheasants to settle down after the disturbance caused.

The placing of guns should be given careful consideration with regards to public roads, private houses and buildings and telephone or electricity wires. Householders are never very pleased when a pheasant crashes through their greenhouse or shot rattles on their windows. Likewise, the British Telecom complain when their telephone wires are shot through.

If guns are placed in woodland, a clearing (known as a gun stand) should be made to enable the gun to see and shoot at the oncoming birds.

Sometimes it is necessary to double bank guns where there is insufficient distance to spread the guns along in a line. 'Double banking' is unpopular with the guns who draw the rear numbers and should be avoided if possible. Guns should be spaced approximately 35-40 yards apart.

During a drive the keeper must allow for the strength of the wind and observe over which guns the birds are flying. He may need to adjust the heading by controlling the beaters, to ensure that all the guns are given as fair a share of the shooting as possible.

Weather conditions greatly affect the willingness of pheasants to fly. Bright sunshine, especially following a hard frost, usually results in reluctance to fly well. Wind or light drizzle seem to improve the quality. Freshly laid snow can cause disappointing results, but if it is imminent, then the birds fly well.

7.8 Release pens should have a wide feed ride and a variety of cover.

7.9 Partridges and pheasants both relish maize cobs.

7.10 Sewelling is used to prevent birds running out of the side of a drive and to rise birds at a flushing point.

7.11 There should be plenty of low bushes such as elder in the release pen to encourage pheasant poults to roost.

The greatest mystery of all - scent - may be the key to the reason why pheasants handle well or not. When scent is good, pheasants will more frequently run on in front of the beaters, but when it is poor they will tend to tuck up under the cover and be reluctant to take wing.

Siting and erection of release pens

The siting of a release pen should be given due consideration, and many factors must be taken into account.

Oobviously, it should not be erected near to public roads, footpaths, etc., or near to the shoot boundaries.

Access must be available for transporting food and water by tractor or van, and to save time when busy.

The wood itself should be in a sheltered position where pheasants would naturally choose to live. It is not necessary for the release pen to be built in a wood that is a good drive. The pen wood should act as a reservoir from which the pheasants can be drawn out to other coverts or game cover.

The release pen should be sited to include a mixture of habitat. A few clear areas for feeding, dusting, sunning and drying off after rain are required. Ground cover will help to occupy the poults and prevent feather pecking. There should be plenty of bushes such as elder or hazel to provide sufficient low branches for the poults to roost on at the start.

It is not recommended to include a stream or any other source of water inside the pen. Most medication is water-based and should the poults require treatment for an outbreak of disease, this would be a problem. Much time and work is saved if mains water can be laid to the pen from a nearby water trough, using alkathene piping. A ball valve can be fitted into a tank in or near the pen from which water can be used. The tank must be kept covered to prevent accidental drowning. If water has to be transported to the pen, five gallon (25 litres) plastic containers can usually be obtained from the farm.

The recommended perimeter size for a release pen is 1 yard per bird, but this can be reduced over 250. Overcrowding must be avoided.

The release pen is best constructed during the late winter or early spring, when the keeper has most time to spare and before the vegetation grows. A wide track should be cleared around the perimeter of the proposed pen. It may be necessary to use some standing trees as posts on which to fix the wire netting. If this is done, the wire must not be nailed or stapled on, but tied with plastic baler twine which can be loosened as the tree grows. Nails, etc., can become imbedded in the trunk and be dangerous at felling time if a chainsaw is used.

Wooden posts can be cut elsewhere or purchased; alternatively, metal posts can be bought. These should be at least eight feet (2.5m.) high so that they can be driven firmly into the ground. They should be spaced about nine or ten feet (3.0m) apart and the corners of the pen must be made rounded. Extra supports may be needed at intervals and at gateways. It is often useful to include two or more gates and to have at least one wide enough to drive a vehicle through. If is it necessary to include corners in a pen for any reason, a removable gate can be incorporated diagonally across the proposed corner. This will prevent poults from gathering in a right-angled corner and can be removed when it is necessary to drive the release pen on a shoot day.

Wire netting needs to be at least six feet (1800mm.) high and of the best quality possible. It is preferable to use half inch to 1 inch (13-25mm) mesh at ground level and up to 3 inch (75mm.) mesh above. Small mesh will help to prevent the poults escaping and predators getting in. If 6 feet (1800mm.) high netting has to be used, this should be no more than one and a half inch (38mm.) mesh and heavy gauge. All joins should be secure. The bottom of the netting should be turned outwards for at least 6 inches (15cms.) to prevent predators digging in. Some keepers also like to have the top turned outwards or put a narrow strip of wire horizontally round the top to prevent cat, fox, etc. from climbing in. There is a difference of opinion as to whether the wire should be left floppy between the posts, to make climbing up difficult, or whether it should be tightened. The turnout at the bottom should either be dug into the ground or pegged down securely. A strand of plain or barbed wire can be strained at ground level to hold the netting in place and another around the top to fasten the netting too. Sloping ground may require a greater height of wire and holes or ditches will need blocking.

The gates should be well made and safely fastened. It is useful to have it opening outwards so that it is easier to drive poults back inside if necessary. A padlock may be desirable if there is any possibility of children or misinformed members of the public letting poults out. A lock is little use against poachers who could readily gain access with a pair of wire cutters. If poaching is likely to be a problem, a security system or deterrent should be installed.

At intervals around the perimeter of the pen, re-entry funnels should be fitted. Particular places where poults are likely to collect is near the gates, at the end of the feed rides and where the fence is curved inwards to the pen. Some funnels may need to be constructed after the poults are in the pen when it is possible to realise where they are most needed. A funnel should be made by cutting a hole in the netting and fitting an anti- predator grid, the bars of which should be three to four inches (8-10cms.) wide. This should allow a twelve week old pheasant to pass through, but not a full grown fox. A wire netting tunnel should be made inside the pen to prevent inmates from escaping. Lead-in wings should be fixed outside, to prevent poults running past the funnel and to guide them back inside.

In areas where predators are prolific, and this includes cats and dogs, it is recommended that an electric fence should be used for protection. In the first instance the outlay may seem expensive, but compared with the expense incurred should a fox or dog gain entry to a pen of wing-clipped pheasants, it is a small premium to pay.

The electric fence should consist of two strands of wire 6 inches and 12 inches (15cms-30cms.) above the ground and about 15 inches (40cms.) away from the wire netting. It is extremely important that the fence is well insulated and there is no contact with the wire netting. Rubber hose pipe can be used as an insulator through the lead-in wings of the re-entry funnels and insulated staples should be used to fix the electric fence wire onto the posts.

Notes on the use of Sprays

The ground vegetation must be kept trimmed or sprayed with **paraquat** beneath the fence to prevent it making contact and shorting out the current. An insulated fastener should be incorporated near the gate if required. A powerful fencer unit should be installed and the fence should be checked to see that it is in working order every time the release pen is visited. A blade or two of grass held in the hand and touched against the wire will minimise the force of the shock and prove that the unit is operational. If the weather is dry, or wellingtons are worn, it may be necessary to put the knee or hand on the ground when the fence is being tested.

Other deterrants such as diesel, flashing lights, radios, scarecrows and empty paper feed bags hung up are all devices that may aid in keeping predators, hawks and owls, etc., away from the release pen.

The *Food and Environment Act,* 1985 covers all usage of sprays and includes the use of knapsack sprayers.

Users are required to be competent in their duties and must comply with the conditions of approval relating to use as stated on the label or in the published approval for the pesticide; i.e., the wearing of protective clothing, application rates, and keeping humans and animals out of treated areas.

Anyone born after 31st December 1964 is required to hold a certificate of competence recognised by the Ministry of Agriculture unless working under the direct supervision of a certificate holder. Detailed records must also be kept of all spraying operations.

Game Crops

Game crops which are usually recommended are as follows:

Artichokes (Perennial)

Canary Grass (Perennial)

Fodder Radish or Mustard (Annual)

Game Crop Mixtures (Annual)

Kale (Annual or Bi-annual)

Maize (Annual)

Millet (Annual)

Shrubs (for woodland planting)

Standing Corn

Stubble

Sugar Beet

Weeds

Game Cover

Many different types of crops are grown for game cover, but perhaps kale and maize are the most popular, preferably grown side by side. Every crop has advantages and disadvantages and no singular one fully combines food and winter cover. Game cover mixtures are marketed that contain several types of plants. Drilling usually has to be left until the risk of frost damage is past, by which time the weather may be dry and germination unsatisfactory.

Soil type, as well as weather conditions, must be taken into account when selecting cover crops.

Game crops are planted either to create a new drive, or to widen an existing one such as a narrow belt of woodland. They should be sited where a hedge or track will provide a link with existing cover. The area should be of sufficient size to hold pheasants, but not so large as to be unmanageable. Existing agricultural crops such as potatoes, turnips, sugar beet, carrots, rape or kale can all be utilised, but may cover such an extensive area that handling and driving is difficult.

Generally, game crops should not be shot late in the day when pheasants will have drawn back to the woodland to roost. (There are occasional exceptions, though, when pheasants will juk in crops such as turnips.) This, of course, does not apply to partridges.

Jerusalem Artichokes should be planted during April in the same way as potatoes. They quickly become established and will provide cover for many years with a minimum of attention. They are only suitable for permanent sites, and may grow very thick. The artichokes may reach a height of eight feet (2.5m.), but the green leaves die back in the winter and the stalks bend over at differing angles. Excessive snow may flatten them, but generally cover is provided through the majority of the shooting season. Pheasants will often unearth and peck at the tubers. The only attention artichokes require is a pre-emergence spraying of paraquat to suppress grass weed growth, although on some soils a dressing of artificial fertiliser may be necessary to promote growth.

Canary Grass is another perennial crop sometimes grown as a game cover. It is difficult and slow to get established and will not flourish on cold, exposed sites. The crop may in time become too dense and the seed heads are of little food value.

Fodder Radish or Mustard is sometimes sown soon after the first crops are harvested, e.g. winter barley or is sown directly into the standing crop about two weeks before cutting. This method allows growth to begin at an earlier date, but germination is very dependent on moist soil conditions. Usually the seed is broadcast and occasionally this is done from the air if sown in standing crops. Fodder radish or mustard can provide cheap and useful cover for early shoots, given the right weather conditions, but it is susceptible to frost damage and soon dies back. It is particularly useful to use as a temporary experiment for siting more permanent crops. Mustard can be grown cheaply and can easily be ploughed back in when it is no longer required. The crop, if sown in June, will develop pods containing seeds that game birds will eat.

Game Crop Mixtures as previously mentioned are produced to provide both food and cover. They usually contain a wide variety of seeds, including maize, sunflower, buckwheat, kale and rape, but once again, results are dependent on having suitable weather conditions to promote germination when the seed is sown. Drilling should take place in May, as some plants contained in the mix are susceptible to frost damage.

Kale is an excellent crop; it is thick enough to make the pheasants less likely to flush all at the same time, it will usually stand all winter, and can be used as cattle or sheep food when no longer needed. The disadvantages are that it may grow too tall or too dense (a problem that can be partially overcome by cutting tracks). Pheasants do not like kale when it is wet, i.e. when raining or after heavy dew or frost, therefore it is best not driven early in the day. Kale is even more attractive if some weeds, especially fat hen, are allowed to grow in the crop. A short-stemmed variety of seed should be chosen to prevent the pheasants running up to the heading too easily.

Kale should be sown during May and will require a further dressing of fertiliser. It should be inspected for insect damage, when spraying may be necessary. If necessary, it can be left to provide cover in the following year.

Maize is a very attractive crop for pheasants and French partridges, who both relish the cobs. However, there are numerous disadvantages and it is really best grown in conjunction with another crop. It is often difficult to get established and, if a particular spray has been used to clear the ground, it may be impossible to grow another crop in its place for at least a year. The drilled seed is attractive to rooks and pheasants, who will go along the rows unearthing it unless it is sown to a depth of at least 10cms. Seed is now available coated with a bird repellant dressing and is well worth the extra cost. Drilling is best left until May when germination should be rapid. Once the critical period is over and the maize is a few inches high, it grows very quickly, even in dry weather. In the autumn the leaves soon die back, providing little cover, the ground beneath is bare, and rooks are attracted to the ripening cobs. The problem of lack of cover can be partially overcome by sowing mustard seed by hand in the heading of the drive during July, if the ground has not been sprayed. Maize is only suitable for growing in the warmer areas of the British Isles.

Millet as game cover is still in experimental stages which were at first disappointing. The seeds are very attractive to pheasants and partridges. This crop requires a mild climate and is therefore only suitable for the more southern parts of Britain. It may prove to be an ideal cover to grow in amongst maize. Millet would provide a denser bottom and the maize would support the millet enough to prevent it getting laid. Further experiments suggest that it is best drilled or broadcast a few days after the maize, around the perimeter or in strips. An extra application of fertiliser may be needed.

Shrubs that are suitable for providing woodland cover are Lonicera, snowberry, box and cotoneaster. Privet and laurel can also be used, but may need controlling to prevent them becoming too dense.

Rhododendron and common privet are best avoided as they may spread quickly and become unmanageable.

Standing Corn if left accidentally or deliberately, will prove attractive to game, although in a wet autumn the ears may sprout. The crop does not stand the weather well, so is only of use early in the season. Excellent pigeon shooting may be had from an area of standing corn in the autumn.

Stubble. Modern farming has greatly decreased the amount of stubbles that remain at the beginning of the shooting season. There is nothing better for holding both pheasants and partridges, which will feed for many weeks on the insects, weed seeds and grain left behind. The haste with which stubbles are burned or sprayed with paraquat seems unnecessary with the efficiency of modern sprays. There is not sufficient cover to make ideal drives, but if the birds can be pushed into a strip of cover, then the results should be very satisfactory.

Sugar Beet is grown extensively in some areas as part of the general farming policy. This crop is extremely attractive to both pheasants and partridges, not only providing cover, but also proving palatable. Harvesting begins in late September. With co- operation from the farmer, the policy adopted is to lift the roots from the headland and then to work roadways across the field. This leaves manageable blocks of cover from which good pheasant or partridge drives may be had. The sugar beet factories remain open until mid-January, so it is possible to have odd blocks of cover left until after Christmas. The chips of sugar beet that are left laid on the ground are readily eaten by game birds.

Weeds Odd patches of weeds are viewed with dismay by farm managers who immediately order the sprayer into action. Weeds are what game birds like, providing both seed and insects. Odd corners of fields or areas of freshly planted trees provide both nesting cover and holding cover later in the year. Fat hen (chenopodium album) is a particular favourite of game and it is surprising this is not grown deliberately as a cover crop. However, a cultivated variety known as 'Quinoa' has recently been introduced and is at present being evaluated.

8
Diseases

Recommended reading:
Game Conservatory Advisory Booklet No. 6
and *Poultry Diseases Under Modern Management* by G.S. Coutts, BVHS, MRCVS
Common Diseases of Game Birds

VIRAL DISEASES
Fowl Pest (Newcastle Disease)
Marble Spleen Disease
BACTERIAL DISEASES
E. Coli (Escherichia Coli, Colisepticaemia)
Mycoplasmosis (Infectious Sinusitis)
(Infectious Synovitis)
Lameness or Cramp
(Staphylococal infection)
Salmonella
T.B. (Avian Tuberculosis)
Yolk Sac Disease

FUNGAL DISEASES
Aspergillosis
Candidiasis (Thrush, Moniliasis)
PROTOZOAL DISEASES
Blackhead (Entero-hepatitis)
Coccidiosis
Hexamitiasis (Trichomoniasis)
PARASITE DISEASES
Gapes (Syngamiasis)
Grouse Diseases (Strongylosis)
MISCELLANEOUS AILMENTS

DIAGRAM OF INTERNAL ORGANS OF GAME BIRD

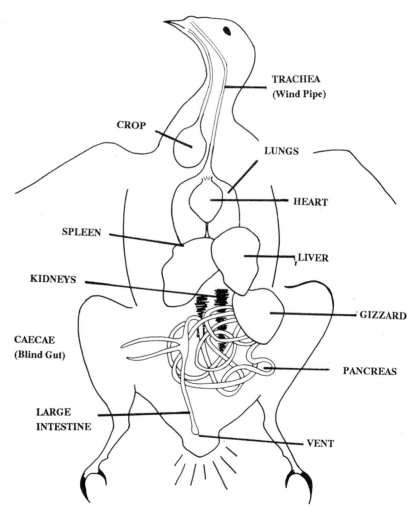

Food is stored in the crop before passing into the gizzard where muscular action and the grit inside break it down. A bird has no stomach

Common Diseases of Game Birds

With artificially reared birds, disease is probably the highest singular cause of losses. Sickness and deaths are obvious on the rearing field and the appropriate treatment should be administered as soon as possible. Losses occurring at a later stage during release are not so readily observed and treatment may prove more difficult. Therefore, it is very important that birds should be in good health and condition when they leave the rearing field.

The more intensive the rearing system, the better the management needs to be. There are many causes of disease, i.e. fungi, parasites, virus, bacteria and protozoa. The risk of infection can be reduced by rearing on fresh ground each year and maintaining a high standard of hygiene at all times. This should begin with care of the breeding stock and continue through incubation, hatching, rearing and releasing

Other than the actual losses sustained, unhealthy birds are more susceptible to further outbreaks of disease, stress, predators and adverse weather conditions. Their growth may also be stunted with the result that they may not be fully mature by the intended shooting dates.

If an accurate diagnosis can be made and a suitable medication is available, then treatment should begin immediately. Even so, a day or two will need to elapse before there is any noticeable improvement.

A sick game bird is easily recognised. It will stand about with ruffled feathers and a general appearance of dejection. When forced to move, its gait will be slow with an exaggerated stride and it may well seek what warmth it can find. Indeed, often the first sign that something is amiss is when young poults are loathe to leave the warmth of the brooder.

Some diseases, such as gapes are easily identified, but others, such as coccidiosis and black head, have similar symptoms at first sight and laboratory tests may be needed to accurately identify the illness. An outbreak of disease can lead to a high percentage of mortality in a short time if left untreated. It is therefore very important to obtain an accurate diagnosis and the appropriate drugs at the earliest possible time. Modern drugs are very effective but it is necessary to carefully follow the manufacturers instructions; low levels of certain drugs are incorporated into some feed rations. This level acts as a preventative and may suppress a minor infection. They are not added at a high enough level to combat a major outbreak of disease though, so further medication will be necessary. The drugs contained in the feed must be taken into consideration when other treatment is administered. The veterinary surgeon should be informed of the drugs used, a list of which will be found on the label attached to each bag of feed. A veterinary prescription is required for drugs supplied for use at a curative level.

When there is any doubt in identifying the infection, expert advice must be obtained, either through the Ministry of Agriculture's laboratories, private laboratories or the Game Conservancy. A fee is charged but this is a small price compared with the potential loss of expensive game birds. Prior arrangements should be made before taking specimens for post mortem. Freshly dead and sick birds, still alive, should be taken. Some diseases are more readily isolated with samples taken from freshly killed specimens. Full background details will be asked for. It is adviseable to make a note of age, place of origin, rearing conditions, feed rations and conditions of management etc beforehand.

Many problems encountered are not directly due to disease, but are caused by poor management and by adverse weather conditions. Some factors can be controlled and careful consideration must be paid to these. By providing the birds with clean living conditions, an adequate diet and sufficient space, losses should be kept to a minimum.

There are numerous diseases that infect chicken and turkeys that can also infect game birds. However, only the ones that are most likely to be encountered by game keepers have been included.

Diseases are often known to the vetinary profession by different names to those with which keepers are familiar, and to denote separate strains of a particular disease. The most common names are used in the text.

VIRUS DISEASES

Fowl Pest (Newcastle Disease)

Duck are not usually affected by this highly contagious disease but outbreaks in domestic poultry or other wild birds can quickly infect game birds. The virus is air borne and there is no effective treatment.

Where there is a serious risk of infection reared game birds can be vaccinated against the disease. This preventative measure should be taken as soon as possible.

Day old chicks are vaccinated by the administration of live vaccine into the eyes using an eye dropper. Further vaccination should be carried out at about three weeks of age either by the same method or by the less accurate method of incorporating the vaccine in the drinking water. Where there is not a high degree of risk of infection the vaccination programme can be delayed until this age.

An injection of dead vaccine, either into the leg or breast muscle or beneath the skin at the back of the head, will provide continued immunity. This should be administered when the poults are released. This method is also used to vaccinate adult breeding stock. The manufacturers instructions must be carefully followed as the vaccine is sensitive to both light and heat.

Fowl Pest symptoms vary as there are several different strains of the disease. It may affect the respiratory tract or in other cases the nervous system. Birds thus affected show signs of staggering, rapid head movements and a crouched position. Water intake may be increased and a green diarrhoea is often present.

Marble Spleen Disease

Several cases have been encountered recently of this virus in pheasants. There are no symptoms and death is sudden. Well grown poults of about fourteen weeks of age may be found dead and deaths may be attributed to some other cause.

When examined it will be noticed that the spleen has a marbled appearance. There is no treatment available. It is difficult to estimate losses with birds of this age as many birds will be out of the release pen by this time, but losses are probably not very great.

BACTERIAL DISEASES

E. COLI (ESCHERICHIA COLI. COLISEPTICAEMIA)

Commonly affects chicks between one and two weeks of age. These show the signs of sickness - dejected appearance etc. Although a post mortem by an expert is recommended a fairly accurate diagnosis can be made by the keeper. When the chick is opened up a mucous like substance will be seen around the heart.

Certain antibiotics are very effective but are only available on prescription from a veterinary surgeon. These are administered in the drinking water. Bacteria are ever present and are not usually harmful unless chicks are exposed to some form of stress eg. over heating, chilling, handling, sickness etc.

MYCOPLASMOSIS

Appears in game birds in two forms:

1. INFECTIOUS SINUSITIS affects the respiratory system. A thin mucous discharge will appear from the eyes and the nostrils. This thickens and large swellings develop under the eyes.

2. INFECTIOUS SYNOVITIS affects the legs causing swelling in the hock joints which prevent the game bird from walking.

In both forms certain antibiotics are effective. However it is often individual birds that are affected and losses are low. Good management and avoiding stress factors are preventative measures.

LAMENESS OR CRAMP this is also caused by staphylococcal infection which gains entry through an injury or cut to the feet. This causes a hot swelling in either one or both hock joints. Resultant deaths are caused by the inability to walk rather than the infection itself. The infection will respond to antibiotics but treatment is not usually economic as there are normally only isolated cases.

SALMONELLA

Is actually a name given to a large group of bacteria consisting of many different strains that can affect animals birds and man in varying degrees. When an outbreak occurs in young chicks losses can be severe. Often the source of infection can be traced back to the hatchery or the breeding stock which may be carriers of the disease.

Although Salmonella can affect birds of any age the most troublesome effect it has as far as game keepers are concerned, is on hatching results and chicks during their first week of life.

Strict hygiene must be enforced both before and after the eggs are set. Eggs should be kept as clean as is possible and washed in an approved egg sanitant if necessary. The manufacturers instructions for strength and temperature of the solution must be carefully followed. Fumigation can be carried out before and during incubation, which will have the dual effect of fumigating both eggs and incubators.

Signs of salmonellosis will become apparent in chicks from about five days of age. Ruffled feathers, a humped up appearance and crowding for heat are the first noticeable signs. Mortality will be high and a post mortem examination should be arranged as soon as possible if salmonella is suspected. Antibiotics can be used as treatment but may result in carriers of the disease surviving and spreading the disease at a later date.

Salmonellosis is highly contagious and appropriate precautions must be taken to prevent the spread of infection.

Hatching results can also be severely affected by the disease which results in death occurring inside the eggs.

Older poults and adults can be affected by other strains of salmonella but it is usually the infection of young chicks that concerns game keepers. Rightly or wrongly they usually share the opinion that duck are a likely source of salmonella infection and are wary of incubating duck eggs in the same incubator as other game bird eggs.

Any poults that have survived an outbreak should be marked, preferably by wing tags, before release. If these birds are caught up later in the season they must not be kept for breeding stock as they can transmit the salmonella infection to their offspring.

T.B. (AVIAN TUBERCULOSIS)

Is infectious, but symptoms do not become apparent until the second year of life, by which time it is so well advanced that treatment is not feasible. The birds may well have been infected early in life. The organism that causes avian tuberculosis can live in the ground for at least two years and is highly resistant to disinfectants.

Serious trouble with T.B. occurs only when birds are permanently penned on the same ground and it becomes continamated. The disease can be prevented by only penning first year stock and by using fresh ground where possible. Considerable losses may be sustained if birds are over wintered for a second year.

Infected birds will become extremely thin. When opened up white patches will be obvious on the liver. By this stage infection will have already been spread via the droppings. As disinfectants have little affect on the organism the only solution is to lime the ground and keep the area free of birds for at least two years. Ploughing and leaving fallow for at least a year is recommended where possible.

YOLK SAC DISEASE

Can be caused by many different strains of bacteria but most commonly it is Escherichia Coli that is the cause.

It has been mentioned previously that losses occur in chicks between one and two weeks old. Yolk sac disease however results in losses during the first few days and is caused by infection via the egg. Bacteria penetrate the shell during incubation which in turn cause the death either in the shell or after hatching. Once again cleanliness at all times is very important in eliminating the disease. Infection can also gain entry through the navel or the respiratory tract. It is not transmitted from chick to chick as such.

Apparently healthy chicks at day old will appear to deteriorate during the next few days. Sometimes growing progressively smaller and weaker and sometimes developing an enlarged abdomen. When opened up the yolk sac, instead of being absorbed, will be present and enlarged. Mortality is variable, reaching a peak about the fifth day. Treatment with antibiotics is usually too late at this stage. Therefore prevention of the disease by strict hygiene and avoidance of stress is the best measure.

FUNGAL DISEASE

ASPERGILLOSIS is caused by fungal spores from mouldy hay, straw, feed, etc. It affects the respiratory tract and, while not passed directly from chick to chick, a large proportion may become infected from the common cause. Birds of any age can become affected.

Incubators may be contaminated, causing infection in freshly hatched chicks. Mouldy hay used in chick boxes is another source. Older poults can be affected by the use of mouldy feed stuffs or by mouldy straw on feed rides.

Symptoms of laboured breathing and gasping are first noticed and, when opened up, the presence of small white spots will be noted on the lungs and respiratory tract.

There is no practical cure and the disease can best be prevented by avoiding any mouldy substances.

MONILIASIS (THRUSH, CANDIDIASIS)

Most commonly affects young hand reared English partridges, but can also affect any game birds reared on grass where the infective fungus is to be found.

On examination, it will be seen that the crop will be coated with a thick white lining.

Prevention by avoiding contaminated grassland is suggested. It was once cured by providing hordes of ants. The modern cure is a solution of formic acid sprayed onto the food.

Diseases caused by Protozoa

PROTOZOA are living organisms that reproduce rapidly and can cause serious losses to game birds if left untreated. There are very efficient modern drugs available that will quickly bring an outbreak under control when administered.

BLACKHEAD (ENTERO-HEPATITIS)

Infection from bird to bird can be a complicated business. Protozoa are eaten by the bird along with food, grit or similar. These increase rapidly in the blind gut (caecal tubes) and are passed out with the droppings. Entry may then be gained into the eggs of Heterakis worms. These are intestinal worms of poultry. Heterakis worm eggs are eaten again along with food, grit, etc., and the process is repeated.

The disease most commonly affects partridges, but can be found in pheasants.

Examination will show that the caecal tubes are affected and severe ulcers and even perforations may be evident. A veterinary post mortem is recommended.

Anti-blackhead drugs (ABH) are often incorporated at a low level in game food rations. This assists in preventing the disease, but will not cure an outbreak. Medication is available on prescription from a veterinary surgeon and is administered in the drinking water.

COCCIDIOSIS is the most common disease encountered by gamekeepers who rear pheasants. It can also affect partridges and grouse in the wild. Curative drugs are available and should be kept in hand.

Infection is once again a complicated process which must be understood.

The eggs (OOCYSTS) are consumed with food, etc. These multiply exceedingly rapidly within the digestive system. Oocysts are then passed out in the droppings and the whole process repeated. The complete process only takes a matter of days, but the rate at which the oocysts multiply quickly spreads contamination. They are also resistant to many disinfectants and can also survive for a long period in the ground. The use of fresh ground each year for rearing and avoiding damp places and a build-up of droppings can help reduce the incidence of disease.

Infection often occurs at about three weeks of age and can be triggered off by wet weather, handling, or other stress. Older poults can be infected too, especially if the release pen used is already contaminated. Pheasants show the usual symptoms of sickness which is often accompanied by a white scour. French partridges frequently show no signs of sickness. The discovery of freshly dead birds, often in good condition, is the first indication of coccidiosis. Losses may be considerable while medication takes affect, and a full course of treatment is necessary to prevent a recurrence. English partridges are not so prone to infection as French partridges or pheasants. When examined, the caecal tubes sometimes contain a cheesy substance, but this is also indicative of some other diseases. Confirmation should be obtained by a veterinary post mortem. However, if coccidiosis is suspected, the appropriate drug should be administered as soon as possible.

Care must be taken in the choice of drug. Most game feed manufacturers incorporate a low level drug treatment in the food (A.C.S.). If certain drugs are administered to treat an outbreak of cooccidiosis, they may combine with those already in the food and produce toxic results. Expert advice should therefore be sought on choice of treatment and dosage reccomendations adhered to.

Care must also be taken if specially produced game rations are substituted by poultry rations. The tickets on the bags of poultry rations should be examined. A warning may appear as to the unsuitability of the ration for game birds. This is because some of the coccidiostats incorporated into poultry feed rations are, may be toxic to game birds.

HEXAMITIASIS is often confused with coccidiosis and, in some areas, it is becoming increasingly common. It usually affects poults of at least five weeks of age, but may be as early as two weeks.

Infection is via the droppings, as with the other protozoal disease, therefore hygiene is important.

The symptoms are similar to coccidiosis, but instead of a white scour, a frothy yellow diarrhoea may be present. Laboratory confirmation is necessary and specimens that are still living should be taken for post mortem. Diagnosis is more difficult after death has already occurred.

Some antibiotics are effective for treating game birds.

TRICHOMONIASIS is very similar to Hexamitiasis, but is more likely to be found in French partridges than in pheasants.

Parasitic Worms

GAPES (SYNGAMIASIS) is a very common problem with game birds. The life cycle of the worm is complicated and it can affect other birds besides game birds.

The female worm attaches itself to the inside of the wind pipe and a male worm attaches itself to her. The eggs they produce are coughed up by the bird, swallowed and passed out with the droppings. These eggs then develop and are either consumed by another bird or ingested by worms, slugs, etc. When this happens, they turn into larvae and may remain dormant for several years.

Eventually the slug or worm is eaten by the bird, the casing of the larva is digested, and the larva released. It will then make its way into the respiratory tract and commence the process over again. Because worms and slugs play host to these larvae, wet places or rain can increase the incidence of gapes by the increased activity of these hosts.

Pheasants and partridges can be seen gasping. Snicking (sneezing) is more obvious in pheasants. If fresh ground is used to rear on each year, then gapes is not usually a problem on the rearing field. The most susceptible period for pheasants seems to be about two or three weeks after being placed in the release pens. Losses can occur in the wild in periods of wet weather on badly infected estates.

Isolated cases in the release pen can be ignored, but a serious outbreak should be treated for several reasons. Apart from potential losses, the disease should not be allowed to build up.

Infected birds will become weak and susceptible to the weather, disease and feather picking.

Highly effective drugs have been developed recently and treatment can either be administered in the drinking water or in the food. Concentrates can be purchased to mix in with the feed or special rations in which the drug is already incorporated are available from game food manufacturers. The feed additive is usually used for ten to fourteen days and is extremely effective. The water-based drugs are usually only administered for one day. Care is needed to give the correct dosage and difficulty may arise with this method. Water consumption will vary daily, depending on weather conditions, therefore providing the correct dosage may not be as accurate as in feed medication. Treatment is expensive, but should not be neglected. It is also recommended for stock birds prior to commencing lay. It will also eradicate all other types of worm.

GROUSE DISEASE (STRONGYLOSIS) is caused by a hair-like worm that affects partridges in the wild as well as grouse. Outbreaks are variable, being worse in some years than others, and occurring in certain areas.

Worm eggs are passed out in the droppings; after a while they hatch and the larval worms make their way onto the underside of leaves of plants. These are eaten by the partridges or grouse and the whole process is repeated.

Losses can be serious and can make a large impact on grouse population. Management of the moor can be an aid to prevention, but other than that, there is little that can be done to combat the disease. By providing good quality heather for feed, the grouse will be kept in the best condition, thus ensuring that the risk of them succumbing to strongylosis is kept to the minimum.

An outbreak of the disease in penned birds can be treated with certain drugs that are used for the treatment of gapes.

SKIN VERMIN

When encountered in penned stock lice, fleas, mites, etc. should be treated with an insecticide powder.

A heavy infestation of ticks can cause serious losses in broods of young grouse. This may be confined to certain localities. Sheep are the main carriers and, although dipping will kill the ticks actually on the sheep, it does little to prevent re- infestation.

MISCELLANEOUS AILMENTS

SPRADDLE LEGS, BENT NECKS AND CROOKED TOES are deformities often caused by a delay in hatching, which causes the chick to be cramped inside the shell. Other cases may be brought about by faulty management. Day old chicks put onto a smooth surface will often develop spraddle legs. Hessian, corrugated paper, wood shavings, pea gravel, etc., are suggested for bedding to prevent this occurring.

STRESS is caused by numerous factors. Handling, extreme weather conditions, etc. There are no specific symptoms, although a general weakness and a white scour may be noted. Birds that are suffering from stress are vulnerable to disease or an outbreak of feather pecking.

IMPACTION OF THE GIZZARD is not a disease, but is common in pheasants, English and French partridge. It can occur at any age, but seems most likely during the first month, when an obsession develops to consume indigestible material. It may be wood shavings, fibres of hessian or string, dried grass roots or stalks, and even small sticks, in fact anything that the bird is able to swallow. There is a general appearance of sickness, wasting and eventual death. On examination, the gizzard will be found to contain a mass of impacted material which effectively blocks the digestive system. Sometimes only individuals are affected whilst, in other instances, several birds will be afflicted. Many theories have been put forward as to the cause, but often there is no apparent reason. Avoidance of stress and the provision of grit and ample food space can help avert the problem. The use of corrugated paper, with plenty of chick crumbs spread on it, in the nursery area for the first few days can eliminate the risk to begin with. However, sooner or later, the chicks will be exposed to some form of indigestible material.

Occasionally it is caused as a result of debility brought about by disease, but more often than not it occurs in perfectly healthy birds.

PROLAPSE of laying birds is fairly common and is usually the result of birds being over fat. The affected hen will be seen to strain and will have, in effect, turned herself inside out. Sometimes the egg will be obvious, hanging from the vent still enclosed in the oviduct. There is no cure, and the hen should be killed to prevent further suffering and perhaps an outbreak of vent pecking.

POISONING Various poisons occur naturally in the wild such as yew. However, most cases of poisoning occur through poults consuming agricultural sprays or seed dressings. Adult birds are equally at risk and some particular sprays and dressings in common use are extremely lethal.

Great care should be taken when using rat poison to ensure that it is inaccessible to any other creatures.

Lead poisoning is often reported in wildfowl, due to the consumption of lead shot in lieu of grit.

SUICIDE The ability of young pheasants in particular to discover ways of killing themselves is amazing. They will swallow great lengths of string, hang in wire netting, drown in an inch of water and smother in corners if either too hot or too cold. Even in the release pen they will hang themselves in wire netting or get caught either by neck or leg in branches. A pheasant knows every way of committing suicide, plus one more, and common sense must be used to eliminate every potential hazard whenever possible.

FEATHER PECKING is often blamed on faulty management. But even when everything possible is done, outbreaks still occur. There is no doubt that overcrowding, excessive heat and, in some cases, light, can instigate an outbreak.

In birds of a few days of age, feather picking often starts on the shoulders, tail or head. Melanistic pheasant chicks are usually attacked on the few white wing feathers that develop. Young partridges are also noted for pecking at the nostrils or toes. In older poults pecking usually begins with the removal of the back feathers, which is difficult to detect, as the wings often cover this area. Pheasant poults in the release pen more often than not pull out the tail feathers. Even though this will lead to some loss of blood, the birds do not seem to suffer unduly, providing the body feathers are left alone, and cannibalism or vent pecking does not develop.

Wherever possible, steps should be taken to prevent or control feather pecking. Good management plays a large part in prevention. De-beaking and the use of plastic bits is also recommended. A general policy with pheasants is to de-beak at ten days of age and to insert either plastic or metal bits at three to four weeks of age. These must be removed when the poults are transferred to the release pens. Spex can be used on adult birds.

A badly pecked poult will suffer loss of body heat and will be vulnerable to heavy rain and cold. Birds so affected will also be at risk to the effects of other diseases.

Vent pecking is the most dangerous form of feather pecking. When an outbreak occurs it must be dealt with quickly, because few birds recover when attacked.

PANIC

Panicking is common amongst large groups of partridges. For no apparent reason they will begin to run around the enclosure and pile into the corners, where they may be liable to suffocate. This phobia does not usually occur until the poults are several weeks old. It is most common in English partridges and losses may be considerable from stress, exhaustion or suffocation.

Little can be done to stop panicking, although spraying them with water may help. Rearing partridges in small groups is probably the best prevention, but obviously this is difficult where large scale rearing is practised.

9
Poaching

9.1 Lurchers are often used by poachers for catching hares and deer.

9.2 A sitting target for poachers. Pheasants should be discouraged from roosting within sight of a road.

Poaching is harmful

Poaching is often portrayed as a harmless and glamorous art. In truth it is certainly not. Poachers are nothing but callous, inhumane thieves. This romantic and cunning image has been intensified by the publication of many books on the subject. These villains when apprehended usually threaten the keeper, his family, or his property and in many cases do actually cause damage.

The number of poachers detained who are eventually brought to court vary in different parts of the country, depending on how rural the area is. Continual co-operation from the local police is necessary before any prosecutions are made. Country police forces are often more fully aware of the cruelty and danger caused by poaching than are urban forces. Therefore, the co- operation is often greater.

Urban police often seem to regard it as a minor infringement of the law and show little interest in bringing about the detention or prosecution of these criminals. Likewise, penalties that are enforced when a poacher appears in court are often ridiculously light where there is no understanding of countryside matters.

Poaching is no longer confined to taking fully grown game. Incidents are reported each year of thefts from aviaries, the rearing field and the release pens.

Keepers of any ilk are harassed by poachers at some time or other. Many, many hours are spent both day and night in attempting to deter or apprehend the culprits. It is not the old fellow who occasionally bags a rabbit for the pot that causes concern, but the organised gangs of criminals who make profit out of poaching. The regular pot hunter, too, can cause serious losses during the season. Nothing is safe; deer, hares, game birds and fish are all deemed worthy of attention.

Many different methods are used, but nearly all involve the use of a vehicle in some form or other, and it is in this department that more help could be forthcoming from the police.

Poaching is no longer carried out under the cover of darkness, but is blatantly practised during daylight. Wherever there is deer or game within shooting distance from a road, the opportunity is there. Modern wildlife, while instantly alert at the sight of a human figure, does not yet regard a vehicle as a potential danger. Because of this, poaching from the window of a car is made so easy; often hasty shots are fired and badly wounded creatures escape.. No effort is made to search for the victims for fear of being caught.

This is not a chapter in which to discuss methods of poaching, but it is certain that almost every technique involves a great degree of cruelty. Snares that are set are not regularly visited, creatures that are shot at, using a beam of light in the darkness, are often not found. The suffering that many of these creatures experience is intense, and feelings would run high against poachers were more people aware of the facts. There is continued lobbying to ban hunting, yet this would be considered humane compared with the indiscriminate use of lurchers to run down deer or farm livestock as practised by some poachers.

The laws dealing with poaching are extremely complex and some date back to the early eighteen hundreds. These are summarily dealt with in a later chapter.

Poacher Deterrents

Several methods of poacher deterrent are available, but there is really no substitute for the constant vigilance and presence of the keeper. The ancient deterrent of the man trap is no longer legal, although many a keeper wishes it were.

Alarm guns and mines have been popular for many years. These are simple devices operated by a trip wire. They were once loaded with nails or shot aimed at the intruder, but now it is only legal to use blank cartridges. These can either be purchased or the shot emptied from live cartridges. Black powder blanks make a louder bang, which must be un-nerving for a poacher who relies on remaining undetected. So far as the keeper is concerned, the disadvantage of alarm guns is that they only emit a single bang, which may easily not be heard or may be difficult to place. Similar devices are also manufactured that release a rocket or a flare.

Increasingly more sophisticated devices are being marketed. In comparison, they are expensive, but offset against the potential loss of game, particularly in areas where poaching is rife, they can soon pay for themselves.

Shoot owners are often reluctant on such an outlay, but until investing in one, do not realise the extent to which poaching has been taking place on their shoot.

The modern electronic systems incorporate sensors of one type or another. Some operate on radio signals, others on pressure, light or heat sensors. Miles of wire back to the keeper's house are no longer necessary. An example of a modern unit consists of a small receiver that can clip onto the belt. The sensor unit complete with aerial is set to shine an electronic beam across a ride or similar area. When this beam is broken a signal is transmitted to the receiver within an area of up to four miles.

The benefit of these systems is that they are small and are inconspicuous, especially in the dark. The poacher is completely unaware that his presence has been detected and the keeper has the element of surprise in his favour.

Apprehension

It is necessary, before charges can be brought about, to catch the offender either in the act of, or in possession of certain items. Being forewarned of the intruder, a keeper has time to summon the assistance of the police. When the poacher is aware that he has been detected, as with alarm guns, etc., there is ample time for him to escape or hide any incriminating evidence before the arrival of the keeper or police.

More and more electronic and radio systems are being produced and installed by estates. Hopefully, as convictions increase, the idea of easy money to be had from poaching will decrease.

A further development is the production of image intensifiers, whereby night vision is produced. Although very expensive at present, no doubt modern technology will lower the price as methods of production are refined and demand increases. This device is of dubious value to keepers, as it will also benefit poachers, who will welcome the opportunity to see in the dark.

Other Deterrents

A German Shepherd Dog (Alsatian) or similar guard dog can be useful for personal protection when dealing with poachers. It is a good deterrent and there are few people who will willingly become involved with a snarling dog. It is very unwise for a keeper to carry a gun when on poacher patrol.

Sometimes a few guinea fowl are put in the release pen with the pheasants. Like domestic geese, they are good watchdogs and react vocally when disturbed. Although creating quite a din, unfortunately they do not confine this reaction to foxes and poachers, so are of little value as deterrents. They also fly badly and can cause embarrassment to guns and pickers up when flushed from a drive. Furthermore, their agitated chattering can result in the pheasants flushing all at once when a shoot is in progress.

All these devices have their uses, but it still needs the observation and common sense of the keeper to catch poachers. Pheasants and partridges should be driven in, off roads and roadside hedges, whenever possible. They should also be discouraged from roosting within sight of a road. Release pens should be situated away from public places.

The new style three strand electric sheep fencing has proved useful in discouraging the use of lurchers, and strands of barbed wire a few inches above the ground are equally effective.

The time that a keeper is in any particular area should be varied, because a regular routine will soon be noted. Frequent sighting of a keeper either on foot or in a vehicle will often dissuade the casual poacher.

It is soon transmitted amongst poachers whose estate it is unwise to visit; likewise, the regular visit to a pub by a keeper will soon be known and plans made accordingly.

Numbers of suspect cars should be noted, although in many cases ownership cannot be traced as the car will still be registered in a previous owner's name. Any car that has been parked for a while should be investigated, although most times this results in being sworn at by the courting couple within!!

The netting of partridges was, and still is, prevented by sticking in branches across the fields.

The discovery of feathers, fresh blood, spent ammunition or a strange footprint must immediately arouse the suspicion that poachers have been about.

Fish Poaching

Fish poaching is a major problem and, like large scale deer or game poaching, is organised by gangs. In some areas it is on such a vast scale that it is seriously affecting stocks, in particular the illegal netting of salmon.

Poison, lines and nets are all used extensively and continual watch by river keepers is needed to safeguard their stock.

All the devices available to the gamekeeper can be of great value to the river keeper.

Some river keepers benefit from extra powers granted to them by the police. They are issued with cards which increase their legal rights to detain suspects. It is a pity that a similar scheme is not extended to approved gamekeepers who, so often, lack sufficient power to enforce the law. Technically it is possible for the poacher to have a greater right to prosecute the keeper than the keeper has to prosecute the poacher in some instances.

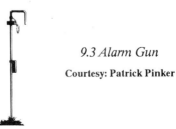

9.3 Alarm Gun

Courtesy: Patrick Pinker

10
WILD PARTRIDGE

Recommended reading:
A Partridge Year by E. Lynn-Allen
and A.W.P. Robertson

10.1 Grey or English Partridge

10.2 French Partridge

Photo: Courtesy Mr. C. Knights

SHOOTING SEASON 1 SEPT - 31 JAN

GREY OR ENGLISH PARTRIDGE (PERDIX PERDIX)

Range covers nearly all of Great Britainbut numbers are declining. Small numbers are reared and released usually from imported stock. Grey partridges pair up in January and are very territorial. Up to 20 eggs are laid in a nest on the ground and are covered with dried grass and leaves. The incubation period is about 24 days by the hen only. Hatching usually takes place during June, both parents tend the young. The family group is known as a covey. The chicks feed only on insects and larvae to begin with before seeds, green stuff, etc. are included in the diet.

FRENCH OR RED LEGGED PARTRIDGES (ALECTORIS RUFA)

The natural range is in England only extending as far north as Yorkshire. They are reared and released extensively. French partridges pair up in March and nest between April and June. The nest is made on the ground but unlike the grey partridge, the eggs are not covered. Incubation is 23 to 24 days and both parents share this and rearing the chicks. Up to 15 eggs may be laid.

GREY PARTRIDGE

BASIC FORMULA

A combination of three factors are required to establish and maintain a successful wild partridge shoot. An expert conscientious keeper, a sympathetic farming policy and ideal weather. If this combination does not exist then the proposition is doomed to failure. It is necessary to have all three factors or else the one that is lacking cancels out the benefit of the other two.

Presuming that a good keeper is employed it must be considered that the land needs to be owned and farmed by the person who shoots it. There is little chance that tenant farmers would co-operate sufficiently towards creating the right environment in which the grey partridge would thrive.

The value of experience gained by partridge keepers over the years has been confirmed by Game Conservancy trials as to the basic requirements.

HABITAT

To begin with field size is important preferably averaging no more than 25 acres. Prairie farming is catastrophic as far as partridges are concerned. The fields should ideally be bordered by hedges 2.5 - 4 metres high and set on banks. Thorn is the best to promote insect life. It is even better if there are tracks between the hedges. A metre wide bank either side of the hedges should be left uncultivated to provide nesting cover and encourage insect life. A narrow cultivated strip is also recommended around the perimeter of the crops to allow a relatively clear area where chicks may dry out after rain and move freely.

AGRICULTURAL REQUIREMENTS

The use of sprays is of particular importance and if possible an unsprayed strip should be left round the outside of each field. Some fungicide and insecticide sprays and dressings are extremely damaging to game and must be avoided. Research has produced effective sprays that are less harmful to game and these should be selected for use.

Research is continuing to evaluate weed growth and the subsequent increased insect levels that will benefit the survival of the grey partridge.

Care of hedgerows is not only important in providing suitable nesting cover but also for the presentation of birds on a shoot day. These hedges may be left to attain a height of 3-4 metres or more, being cut back every third year. Where double hedges exist either side of a track this can be done by rotation. The sides are trimmed back annually to ensure an adequate growth of ground vegetation to supply nesting cover and shelter.

The farming policy should be geared to promote chick survival. Young partridge chicks feed entirely on insect life when first hatched, the presence of which is therefore absolutely crucial. Continual wet weather too can be a killer both before and after hatching. Leaving areas free of vegetation will provide space for the sitting bird to dry off within the vicinity of nests. It also means that access is available for the keeper to tend to traps and keep a watch on nests.

PREDATOR CONTROL

Control of vermin is a partridge keeper's priority throughout the year. In late winter and the spring it will be given sole attention. Ground vermin especially small animals such as rats, stoats and hedgehogs are a great danger to nesting partridges. As hedgehogs hibernate control is not practical until later in the spring. Foxes are a cause of major concern on a partridge beat, but are often less common where partridges thrive. Magpies too seem less common and no doubt the absence of these two extremely destructive predators has much to do with partridge survival. Feral cats and winged vermin, particularly crows, must also be strictly controlled.

TRADITIONAL STANDARDS

At one time a devoted partridge keeper would tolerate neither pheasant or french partridge on his beat and would destroy the nests of both should he find them. The grey partridge was an obsession with him and its welfare throughout the year was his sole occupation. This beat was known as a partridge manor in days past.

MODERN CONDITIONS

There are very few wild partridge shoots today and even on these estates the keeper is expected to present french partridges and later on pheasants for the shoot.

The usual policy on such estates is to shoot pheasants as hard as possible during the season and to leave little stock. Poults are purchased during July and August to provide the season's sport. There is no doubt that hen pheasants will interfere with partridge nests if they discover them and are a nuisance during the breeding season. Wild french partridge also have to be tolerated.

WEATHER EFFECT ON BREEDING SUCCESS

The third factor to be taken into consideration for partridge survival, and one over which there is no control, is the weather. Late spring and early summer are the vital periods. If the weather is unfavourable prior to hatching, insect life will not be abundant enough to support the young chicks. Warmth and moisture are both required but prolonged wet weather or torrential rain may cause the sitting hen to desert her nest or the young chicks to drown.

Traditionally grey partridges hatch during Royal Ascot race week and therefore the weather throughout June has the most critical effect on survival.

DISTRIBUTION AND MANAGEMENT

Grey partridge will pair as early as December but, during January, if the weather is harsh, they may reform into coveys temporarily.

A spring partridge count is conducted at the end of March before the crops grow too tall. By this time pairs of partridges will have stablished their territories. The count is done in the early morning or late evening from a vehicle, preferably when the ground is dry enough to allow access to all parts of the shoot.

The resultant figures will establish the pattern and density of the breeding stock. A pair to every five acres is the ideal but this is rarely achieved. Numbers of pairs may fluctuate yearly on any one beat. There appears to be a mysterious cycle whereby an area will become good over a few years and then slowly decline again to such a low level that shooting is impractical. After this trough has been reached the area equally mysteriously improves until a peak is obtained. There is no apparent cause but this is a recognised syndrome. Breeding stock seems unable to thrive and resultant deaths occur. Despite extensive research into health, the use of chemicals and cropping patterns, no cause has yet been identified. During late April and May the hedges will be walked and nests located and noted. Unlike pheasants and french partridges, the grey cover their nests until the clutch is completed. It is therefore not so easy to detect a nest and often the track leading through the vegetation to it is what first attracts the attention. The eggs are uncovered immediately prior to sitting and a further egg is often added to the clutch after incubation has commenced.

Eggs from nests in potentially dangerous positions, for example, beside well used footpaths, may be picked up and hatched artificially. Some keepers also favour reducing the number of eggs from within the nest from possibly as many as twenty down to about twelve. The assumption being that parents are more likely to rear a dozen successfully than they would coping with as many as twenty. At these times a few broody bantams are invaluable but incubators can also be used successfully to hatch the surplus.

In some areas the **Euston system** is practised. This is the name given to the following method:

The partridge is allowed to lay approximately six eggs which are then replaced by nine or ten dummy eggs. Further eggs are picked up as they are laid and a note is made of the date the bird begins to sit. When the time is due that hatching should take place the dummy eggs are replaced with eggs that have been artificially incubated and are at the chipping stage.

This system almost eliminates the risk to a nest during incubation and should misfortune fall on the sitting hen at least the eggs will be safe. No scent is emitted by a sitting bird until the last few days of the incubation period. Nests are often not detected by predators until this final stage has been reached, so this is the critical period during incubation.

Artificial incubation and rearing is dealt with in another chapter as are broody hens and bantams.

Known nests are monitored but it is impossible to discover every one. Tragedies occur during the nesting season. Hens are killed by predators or accident. Road deaths and disturbance caused by farm work are inevitable and some sprays and dressings will cause poisoning. Broody bantams are also

10.3 Unlike English partridge, the nest of French partridge are left uncovered.

10.4 Nesting French partridge exposed due to agricultural spraying.

particularly useful at this time when partially incubated nests may have to be picked up.

During June the highest proportion of nests will hatch and hopefully previous weather conditions will provide an ample supply of insects. Torrential or a lengthy period of cold rain may decimate broods at this stage but adequate hedgerow cover should afford some protection.

Artificially incubated eggs will also be hatching during June and some work will be necessary on the rearing field.

Vermin control is still of great importance as chicks will be particularly vulnerable until they can fly.

By the time the broods are a month old a rough estimate can be made of breeding success, but corn will be standing and coveys difficult to locate.

It is beneficial if road and track verges are kept trimmed along either side. This should already have been done before nesting commences and, after hatching, this will provide an area where broods can rest or dry off without having to stray onto the road where they are at risk.

Immediately prior to harvest it may be possible for the partridge keeper to have some respite from the work and even to take a few days' holiday.

As the corn is cut the estate will be opened up and a better idea of breeding success will be gained. The keeper may be involved with straw burning operations and he will certainly be keeping a watchful eye on fields where the combines are at work, both with a view to partridge numbers and the presence of vermin.

When the harvest is near completion a further count will be taken in the middle of August. Records will be made and the ratio of young birds to old will be worked out. This allows a more accurate assessment to be made of the results of the breeding season and the potential for shooting.

The partridge shooting season opens on September 1st but there are few shoots that start as early as this and many leave it as late as October before beginning. In a bad year the decision may be taken not to shoot at all if there is insufficient stock.

By the end of August when access is possible into most fields the reared partridge poults will be about ten weeks old and ready for release. This can be done by the conventional method of putting small groups out in sectional pens as described in Chapter 6. Some partridge keepers where possible prefer to release coveys of up to twenty in a territory occupied by a barren pair of grey partridges. The keeper will already have observed where these pairs are. A small sectional pen is erected and the partridge poults placed inside. In most cases it is not long before the barren adults show an interest in the young birds. As soon as it appears that the pair have adopted the covey

10.5 Day old English partridges are very small.

10.6 Broody bantams are invaluable for hatching small numbers of partridge eggs

as their family then they should be released and the pen removed. Occasionally either a cock or a hen may adopt a covey on their own.

Releasing by this method appears to be best where there are sufficient pairs of barren grey partridge. It is surprising from what distance they will come to attach themselves to the young birds. Once adopted the covey will soon adapt to life in the wild and, with their foster parents acting as an anchor, should be less likely to stray or amalgamate with other coveys.

It is advisable if possible to only supplement the wild stock with young hatched from eggs picked up on the estate. Many grey partridges sold by game farms are hatched from imported eggs. By avoiding the introduction of these, a pure strain will survive on the estate that has adapted itself well to local conditions.

SHOOT GUIDELINES

During September the keeper will be assessing the distribution of partridges and planning his shoot days. Account must be taken of agricultural crops that have not yet been harvested such as sugar beet. Small areas are useful for heading a drive from as the coveys will be more likely to break up among the cover. Large fields however must be avoided as once the partridges have found refuge there, it will be impossible to drive them out again when the beaters are far apart.

With the co-operation of the farm manager many stubbles will still remain although of necessity some fields will have already been cultivated.

The drives will be carefully planned and pegged out. Allowance will have to be made for wind strength and direction and alternatives must be made available. Poor results will be achieved if partridges are driven into a cross wind without due allowance being made with regards to heading the drive.

In some open areas it may be necessary to build hides or butts beforehand to conceal the waiting guns.

The drives should not be too long, a suggested maximum is 100 - 150 acres but the contours of the ground and underfoot conditions must be taken into consideration. Partridges will run or fly in front of the beaters but they soon tire if an attempt is made to drive them too far.

The drives should be planned to present the partridges over the guns in the best possible way. A high hedge and the guns stood back on ground that slopes away will give extra height and speed. By heading the drive from a small area of roots, or other cover, the coveys will be more likely to split up and come over the guns a few at a time. Few birds will be shot if all the partridges in a drive rise together and fly over the guns in one mass.

Prior to a shoot day beaters, pickers up and transport will have to be arranged. On the actual day it is very important that everyone is familiar with the day's plans. The most reliable beaters will be put on the flanks, for it is their responsibility not to allow the birds to break out of the sides of the drive. Flags will be handed out and instructions given on their use. These are most effective when waved in a figure of eight motion and not until the partridges rise. Flags are used to turn the birds in the desired direction. The sudden appearance of one is far better for doing this than one waved continuously. Hand held radio sets are often used and are very useful in directing the flankers from the centre of the beating line.

Flag men may need to be placed on roads or tracks to prevent the birds from flying along them. Gateways and gaps in hedges are both places where partridges may tend to channel through instead of staying spread out. These should have been blocked with fresh cut branches a day or two beforehand where necessary.

Observation and experience will uncover the route the partridges prefer to fly in when disturbed. It is worth noting this during normal working operations and taking it into account when planning a drive.

ANALYSING THE RESULTS

When the shoot day is over the bag is usually inspected and a note made of the proportion of young to old that have been shot. An experienced game cart man may have already done this when tying and hanging up the partridges. The most reliable means of identification is made by inspecting the primary wing feathers. On young birds these will be pointed whilst on the old birds they will be blunt and rounded.

By November partridge shooting should be almost completed as by this time they will have become difficult to handle and present over the standing guns. It is necessary to preserve a balanced breeding stock. The number of shoot days must be planned with this in mind. In a poor year when stocks are low then shooting should be curtailed. In a good year extra shooting should be arranged because it is impractical to leave a surplus over a certain number. The grey partridge is very territorial and only a certain density of breeding pairs will be successful. An allowance must however be made for natural wastage during the winter.

Supplementary winter feeding is only advisable during severe weather conditions. Deep snow should be cleared in places and a light sprinkling of wheat made available.

10.7 An overgrown hedge can be ideal to drive partridges over.

10.8 Partridge shooting country. Stubbles and hedges.

FRENCH OR RED LEGGED PARTRIDGES

The French partridge despised so much by old time keepers has now to be accepted. Conditions that are created for the welfare of the grey partridge will also benefit the survival of the French population. In recent years the French or Red Leg partridge as it is often called, has become very popular with game farms. Many shoots release them to supplement pheasant shooting and to extend the season. Many of these so called partridges are, however, hybrids of imported strains. These are sometimes known as chukar types or ogridges and do not breed very successfully in the wild. They are best viewed on a 'put and take' basis. The true French partridge is more successful and if stock is purchased with the intention of building up a wild population then this should be remembered. The hybrids have become most popular with game farms because they lay more eggs and are easier to rear. Hybrids can be identified apart from the true French as they lack the black speckle markings that extend from the throat to the chest on the true French. Closer inspection will reveal that true French possess only one dark band on the flank feathers while hybrids possess two.

Although French differ slightly to the Grey in habits the same principles apply in maintaining a good stock, i.e. vermin control, co-operation with farming interests over usage of sprays and agricultural operations and of course kind weather. The French partridge lays its eggs in an uncovered nest and hatching takes place over a more extended period than with the Grey, thus the weather may not be quite so critical at a certain time. The French are happy to stay on cultivated ground and in the winter may appear on woodland rides where pheasants are fed. Unlike greys, they will often nest on the edge of woods, sometimes sharing a nest with a pheasant. It is also quite common to see them perched on roofs, fences, branches or jukking on straw stacks. But mostly they are judged by shooting men on their flying ability. It is here that a comparison is made and the French is found inferior. There is no sight like a covey of Grey partridge bursting over a high hedge at speed and fully testing the waiting guns.

CONCLUSION

The Grey partridge is in steady decline. It is the jewel in the crown of any shoot and every effort should be made to preserve it. The Grey, though a small bird, possesses immense character and very strong family ties. Anyone who has had the chance and taken the time to study the English partridge cannot fail to respect it.

Constant research is being carried out into reasons for the decline and many causes can be identified. But as yet there is no answer and the decline continues.

10.9 Partridge shooting in late September.

(Courtesy Mr. M. Wingrove)

11

GROUSE

My grateful thanks to Mr. Bryan Burrows, Head Keeper to Lord Peel at Gunnerside, North Yorkshire for explaining to me the work involved and providing some of the photographs.

Recommended Reading

Game Conservancy Booklet No. 12

11.1 Grouse on the moor

Illustration: J.G. Millais

GROUSE KEEPING

SHOOTING SEASON (DATES INCLUSIVE)

Grouse   August 12 - December 10
Ptarmigan   August 12 - December 10
Black Game August 20 - December 10
Capercaillie October 1 - January 31

RED GROUSE (LAGOPUS LAGOPUS)

The species of grouse that is associated with traditional grouse shooting is the red grouse. A bird that is unique to Britain. The male is about fifteen inches (38 cms) long and weighs approximately one and a quarter pounds (600-700g). The female is slightly smaller. The plumage is a mottled reddish brown, the hen birds are a lighter colour and the feathers are more heavily barred. Legs and feet are lightly covered with pale hair like feathers. Cock birds possess a red comb above each eye.

The eggs are laid in a scrape in the ground, lined with grass or heather during April and May. Averaging between six and twelve they are incubated for twenty two days. The hen only sits but both parents tend the chicks.

The range of the red grouse is confined to heather covered moorland. Although odd pockets exist in other parts of the British Isles, they are generally found in parts of Wales, Ireland, Northern England and Scotland.

The staple diet is heather with the addition of berries, seeds and flowers.

PTARMIGAN (LAGOPUS MUTUS)

Ptarmigan are closely related to the red grouse, but are only to be found on high ground over two thousand feet. Their range is confined to the Scottish mountains, but they also inhabit other countries within the Northern hemisphere.

11.2 Ptarmigan

11.3 Black grouse (Blackcock)

Photos: Courtesy Mr. C. Knights

Ptarmigan are similar in habits and size to red grouse. Their plumage however changes to white in the winter, apart from retaining some black tail feathers. During the summer the wings remain white while the body plumage is darker.

BLACK GROUSE (LYRURUS TETRIX)

Black grouse are better known as blackcock or greyhens. The hen bird is similar in size and appearance to the red grouse. However the blackcock is larger and possesses distinctive glossy blue-black plumage.There is a white bar on the wings and the underside of the tail is white. This is raised during the courtship displays which are enacted on communal display grounds known as 'leks'. The diet of black grouse consists of insects, conifer shoots and the leaves of plants etc. Because of their taste for conifer shoots they are unpopular with foresters. The range of black grouse is limited to Wales, Northern England and Scotland although a few pairs exist in certain other areas. They also breed in other North European countries.

The eggs are laid in a scrape in the ground during May or June. The young are tended by the female only.

CAPERCAILLIE (TETRAO UROGALLUS)

Capercaillie are large birds, the cock being about thirty three inches (84 cms) in length and weighing anything up to fifteen pounds in weight (7 Kgs). The hen is slightly smaller. They are similar in appearance to the black grouse but the cock bird lacks the white beneath the tail. Like the black grouse they also feed mainly on conifer shoots, Capercaillie are only to be found in forests in Scotland, but they also breed in other Northern European countries. During the late eighteenth century capercaillie became extinct in the British Isles, but were successfully re- introduced in the mid-nineteenth century.

The eggs are laid in a scrape in the ground lined with vegetation, during April or May. The female only tends the young.

THE GROUSE KEEPER

The duties of a grouse keeper are concerned with providing the right environment in which the grouse will flourish. They cannot be artificially reared with any success, so that in order to provide shooting great care must be taken to create the correct habitat.

Grouse shooting provides a source of sport and income from areas of the British Isles that are virtually useless for agriculture. Moorland which is bleak, windswept and covered with heather is only suited to grazing by sheep. Where the land is overgrazed grouse stocks will suffer due to shortage of food. The use of sprays is virtually unknown in these areas so there is no threat to grouse from this hazard as there is to partridge stocks.

Although success is partly dependant on the weather conditions there are other factors involved that a keeper has control over. Of particular importance are predator control and the burning of heather.

HEATHER MANAGEMENT

Heather is the main source of feed for grouse and its management is of vital importance. Burning is carried out to ensure the continued availability of young heather for feeding and older heather for nesting cover. Grouse are strictly territorial and therefore each territory needs areas suitable for nesting and feeding within it. Territories usually cover an area of at least five acres, they are fought for throughout the autumn and winter and are closely guarded. Harsh weather may however cause grouse to move temporarily. Because of their competitive habits it is necessary to burn many small strips in different areas rather than a few large patches.

There are legal limits on times when burning can take place according to individual areas, but generally it is between the end of October until mid April. If the grouse nest early it may be necessary to stop before this date. Although this appears to be a long period in which to achieve the desired amount there are relatively few days that are actually suitable for burning. Great care has to be taken to ensure that the ground is cleaned properly. If the moor is burned too fiercely the heat will kill the roots of the heather. Too cool a fire will result in insufficient clearance of the old vegetation and this will impair fresh growth. To attain the correct intensity of fire the weather conditions need to be ideal. Dampness and wind can result in an insufficient burn. Burning after a long spell of dry weather may cause too hot a fire and may even set the underlying peat alight. Small areas are burned on a seven to ten year rotation, according to heather growth, to give the best results.

Heather damage on many moors is caused by overgrazing. If co-operation is not forthcoming from the moor owner in limiting the stocking rate of sheep there is little the keeper can do. Where stocks are kept to an acceptable level they can be incorporated into moor management but, generally speaking, the sheep is an animal that the grouse keeper would sooner be without on his moors. Not only does overgrazing affect the immediate availability of food for grouse, but it can also damage the plant, so weakening it that other vegetation of no value such as bracken will predominate.

11.4 Heather burning plays an important part in grouse management.

(Courtesy Mr. B. Burrows)

11.5 Grouse are very territorial..

PREDATOR CONTROL

Apart from heather burning, the most important factor in moor management is predator control. Foxes and crows are usually the main enemies of nesting grouse. Hooded crows are particularly vicious and can cause serious damage not only to grouse but to sheep on the moor. Their despicable habit of removing the eyes of young lambs or weak adults should ensure that their presence is unwelcome by keepers and shepherds alike. Fox control also benefits the shepherd as on open moorlands lamb makes a tempting meal for a hungry fox.

The control of winged vermin is legally limited to either trapping or shooting. Cage traps should be set up and baited several days prior to setting. A dead sheep may prove an attractive bait. Decoys such as stuffed owls can be used to entice crows within shooting range.

Protected birds of prey such as hen harriers and buzzards can cause losses and their presence on a shoot day may be responsible for spoiling a drive. The appearance of a hawk may cause the grouse to squat close to the ground and be reluctant to move. It may even cause the grouse to vacate the area completely.

Moorland foxes are prolific and can cause serious damage to stocks particularly during the breeding season. Snaring is impractical due to the presence of sheep therefore other methods must be employed. These methods inevitably involve many miles of walking.

When snow is laying it is often possible to track a fox for many miles. Hopefully this will lead to where it has chosen to lay up for the day or to where it may have cubs. Piles of rocks, drains, peat runnels (where water has run out of sight beneath the ground) must be inspected regularly. A detailed and intimate knowledge of the moor is imperative to locate litters. Cubs are often born on lower ground and are moved up to the moors later on. When a vixen and cubs have been dealt with a watch should be kept for the dog fox to return to his family.

In many places it is impossible to gas litters, at such times the services of a good terrier are invaluable. It is advisable to fit a collar incorporating a locating device before entering the dog. Many fell terriers are encouraged to kill rather than evict a fox. Where there is only one exit to a rock pile, drain, etc., a box trap can be left in position to catch the fox.

During the summer foxes will lay out on the moor, beds of bracken being a favourite choice. Drives can be arranged for such areas. Other methods are the use of big strong lurchers that will run down and seize a fox that has been disturbed. Two or three couple of foxhounds can also be employed to locate

11.6 Mosaic pattern on moorland caused by burning areas of heather.

11.7 Line of traditional grouse butts built from stones and capped with turves.

and catch foxes on the open moorland. At night, on such open ground, the use of a strong light and a rifle can also be an efficient method of control.

Small mammals such as stoats are trapped by conventional methods using tunnel or box traps. Stone walls, that are a common feature in moorland areas, provide useful sites for trapping and also materials for building tunnels. In some localities the walls are constructed in such a way that a small open space is left at intervals along the base of the wall. These can be made use of when siting traps.

DUTIES THROUGHOUT THE YEAR

Vermin control is a permanent task, but the grouse keeper's year begins with heather burning. The area the keeper is expected to care for may cover several thousand acres, much of which is not easily accesible other than by foot. A great amount of a moor keeper's time is therefore spent walking.

The weather is the most influential factor over which a keeper has no control. Not only does it have a bearing on the survival of young chicks but previous to that period, it can have a direct effect on grouse stocks. Snow is not particularly harmful, indeed it can act as insulation for the heather against the devastating effects of dry, bright weather accompanied by an easterly wind and near freezing temperatures. It is this combination that causes 'browning' of the heather, resulting in inferior quality feed and grouse coming into the breeding season in poor condition. When this happens hatching results are usually disappointing.

A count is made during April to assess the density of breeding pairs. It is advisable to leave the count until the snow has gone as this may have caused pairs to temporarily vacate a territory. A typically selected area is hunted up with dogs and an accurate count is made of pairs. The same area is counted each year so that a direct comparison can be made.

BREEDING SUCCESS

Eggs are usually laid during April, but as with the heather growth, nesting time may vary according to the individual area and prevailing weather pattern.

The young chicks hatch at the end of May when once again weather conditions play an important role. Prolonged drought at this time of year can affect the hatchability of eggs and the availability of insects which are, at first, a proportion of the chick's diet. Young heather shoots and flowers soon replace insects and become the main food items.

An abundance of insect life is not however of such great importance to freshly hatched grouse chicks as it is to other young game birds. Their survival appears to depend more on the original condition of the parent stock.

Nests are not especially looked for, nor are the eggs picked up and incubated artifically. During normal keepering activities however nests will be located.

The chicks, which grow very quickly, are tended by both parents and can fly short distances at about two weeks of age. Leaves and berries of other moorland plants will supplement the diet of heather where available.

A further count is made during July to assess the breeding success and shooting potential.

DISEASES

Disease is more prevalent some years than others and may have taken a toll of the young birds.

Strongylosis (see P 166) may be present particularly on high wet moors and can have a serious effect where stocking levels are high or where grouse have been in poor condition.

Heavy losses to broods in some areas may have been the result of tick infection (see P 166).

As with partridges there seems to exist a natural rise and decline over several years in grouse populations. Despite continued research and many possible theories no single cause has yet been identified. The result of the July count will determine the number of shoots that are arranged.

Broods averaging eight are excellent, averaging five are moderate, and below is considered poor.

SHOOT GUIDELINES

Grouse shooting traditionally starts on August 12 and most moors begin on this date.

The immediate shooting days will have been decided bearing in mind that it is as damaging to a moor to under shoot as it is to over shoot.

With moors covering such an extensive area and, in many cases, being somewhat isolated it is often arranged to shoot on several consecutive days to cover all the ground. It is a busy time for keepers who not only will have taken constant observations of grouse distribution but may also have to arrange beaters, pickers up and loaders and their accommodation

11.8 Beaters driving grouse over waiting guns.

11.9 A 'gun's' eye view of driven grouse.

(Courtesy Mr. B. Burrows)

Prior to the start of the season the keeper will also have had to renovate the grouse butts and ensure that roadways and bridges are passable to motor vehicles.

In areas where the density of grouse permits they are usually driven over standing guns. A team of beaters will be sent to cover a wide sweep of moorland and head it towards a line of butts placed on natural flight lines. Where grouse stocks are low and this method of shooting is not practical then grouse are walked up. A team of guns and dog men will line up and walk in line across an area. Here certain breeds of dogs come into their own for pointers and setters will range widely. On locating the presence of grouse they adopt a stance indicating a find. This position is held until a further order is given by which time the guns will have come within shooting range.

After each drive the freshly shot game must be protected from flies and a liberal amount of fly spray may be needed.

At the end of the day the bag is carefully sorted to separate the young from the old. These are identified by various methods. The toe nails of mature grouse are shed during the summer. Therefore any sign of detached toe nails will indicate an old bird as young ones do not shed toe nails. The third outermost primary wing feather being shorter than the rest is another indication of a young bird. However the most reliable evidence of age is the comparison of the two outermost primary wing feathers. In the young grouse these are pointed and narrow while in older birds the primaries are broader and more rounded.

Shooting may continue through October if numbers permit and a further day or two may be arranged for farmers and keepers during November if necessary. Days may have been cancelled due to bad weather and it may be disastrous to leave too large a head of stock. Only a certain population level can be successfully supported on any moor. Above this there will be increased pressure for territorial space, resulting in grouse being in poor condition and subsequently more susceptible to disease. It is part of good moor management to reduce numbers sufficiently to leave the maximum acceptable level. Equally it is important not to overshoot in a poor year when stocks should be allowed to rebuild. An allowance has to be made for natural losses that inevitably occur during the winter.

FEEDING

Hand feeding is not practical at any time of the year. The provision of grit is the only aid a keeper can give to the welfare of his stock. Grouse generally seem to find sufficient water even during the dryest spells of weather. However during really prolonged drought it may be necessary for them to search for water which may result in packs forming temporarily in areas where water is present.

DISTURBANCE

Poaching is not generally a problem although inevitably the odd birds are taken by shooting from vehicles where public roads cross moors.

The public do not often cause too much disturbance other than along the sides of public roads and beauty spots. Any walkers on the hill are usually dedicated people who obey the rules of the countryside and normally adhere to defined paths.

The biggest danger to grouse from the public is in the form of a potential fire hazard. When the moorland has become tinder dry after a prolonged spell of dry weather a carelessly thrown cigarette end can be dangerous. Hundreds of acres of unbroken dry vegetation and a stiff breeze can soon render a fire out of control with devastating effect.

Occasionally attempts are made by groups of 'antis' to disrupt shoot days, which can prove a particular nuisance.

Thousands of acres of moorland in England and Scotland have been lost to grouse shooting by overgrazing. It is sheep that are by far the greatest threat to the welfare of grouse.

12
Wildfowl

Recommended reading
Game Conservancy Advisory Booklet Number 3

12.1 Canada Geese (Courtesy: C. Knights)

12.2 Greylag Geese

soon as the tailings are available and should be carried out at the same time each day once a feeding pattern has been established.

As the start of the shooting season on September 1st approaches, a closer watch should be kept on the pond. Signs of dabbled ground, churned up water and feathers will indicate that ducks are visiting. Observation should be carried out at dusk and an evening flight organised as soon as possible when numbers have built to a satisfactory level. Wild duck are fickle creatures and a plentiful supply of grain on stubbles or acorns elsewhere will be enough to stop them appearing regularly.

Numbers fluctuate throughout the season, according to weather and the availability of other food, so the opportunity must be taken when it presents itself.

Hides should be built before the season, and must blend in with the natural surroundings. Even in the half light, a duck has very keen eyesight and the slightest thing out of the ordinary will stop it coming in to the water. For this reason, it is essential to wear well camouflaged clothing and a hat to shield the face.

If the pond is used as a day time resting place by duck, they should be put off during the afternoon so that they will flight back later in the evening to feed.

Decoys and duck calls can be used to attract the ducks over the waiting guns with variable success.

Sometimes morning flights are organised where it proves more effective than evening flighting.

Flighting along rivers is also practised and may involve a few beaters driving the river along towards concealed waiting guns.

Wild fowl are also shot at inland feeding areas such as stubble and potato fields.

Wild duck can be encouraged to breed on ponds, lakes and rivers, by creating suitable conditions. Vermin should be controlled and mink must be eradicated at all costs for they will kill every duckling in the vicinity. Nesting sites should be planned and the provision of some duck nesting baskets will aid success. Mallard have a wide breeding season and will hatch off very early in the spring. These ducklings rarely survive as there is insufficient insect life to sustain them. If it is practical, these early eggs can be collected and hatched artificially. *(See page 313 and Chapter 4)*

Snipe Shooting

Occasionally, snipe shoots may be organised on marshy ground which may be part of a keeper's beat. These little birds are similar in appearance to a woodcock, but are to be found in open areas not in woodland. More often than not, though, they are included in a day's bag when they have been disturbed during a pheasant or partridge drive or when duck shooting.

12.7 Duck hides should be well camouflaged.

13

River Keeping

River Keeping

My grateful thanks to Mr. Ron Wilton, river keeper on the Lower Itchen in Hampshire, for sparing me his time and answering my many questions.

Trout, Salmon, and Grayling

The close season for trout and salmon is through the winter from approximately mid-October to mid-March. Individual areas fix their own dates, but there is a statutory 80 day period that allows for spawning.

Grayling spawn in the spring at the same time as course fish, and share the same close season, mid-March to mid-June.

Duties

A river keeper's duties are varied like those of a game keeper's and the year's work is geared to producing good sport and enjoyment for those who participate.

The river keeper must acquire an intimate knowledge of his stretch of the river. It is his business to be aware of what is happening to both the water and the fish. Daily detailed observation is necessary in maintaining or improving a river to produce a high standard of fishing. Of particular importance is the study of what fish are feeding on. It is not sufficient to just know where the fish are lying; success will only be achieved by the fisherman if he can attract the fish to his hook. For the purist fly fishing is the only approved method of catching game fish, although other ways are acceptable on some rivers. Frequently the river keeper's advice is requested on choice of flies, etc.

Modern pressures have made it necessary for larger stretches of rivers to be tended by one man and hazards such as pollution have increased the need for vigilance.

The Scottish salmon river keeper is called a gillie. While not involved with the river maintenance to the extent that some trout river keepers are, he still

Rainbow Trout

Brown Trout
13.1 Species of game fish.

Courtesy: Mr. P. Mitchener

is expected to advise and assist the fisherman. Sometimes he is employed only for the fishing season which is from January or February through to September or October.

Species of Game Fish

Trout

Game fish that river keepers will be most involved with are trout, salmon and grayling. In the north it is salmon that receive priority treatment and in the south it is trout. Rainbow trout are reared artificially and are not viewed with the same enthusiasm as brown trout by sportsmen. Sea trout (or sewin) are a strain of brown trout that have adopted a life cycle similar to that of the salmon.

Grayling

Grayling, although a worthy game fish, are often controlled in trout streams as they compete with the wild brown trout. They breed prolifically, but they are extremely susceptible to pollution and are a useful indicator as to the health of the river. They also spawn at a different time of the year to other game fish and can provide good sport during the statutory post- spawning eighty day close season for salmon and trout.

Salmon

Salmon have certain times of the year when they 'run'. Early spring is when fresh run salmon may be caught as they make their way upstream. Unfortunately, at this time, spent fish, in poor condition from spawning, will be attempting to make their way back to the sea. These must not be killed.

A spell of rain after a dry spell can also produce sport during the summer months.

The life cycle of a salmon is complex and hazardous. Stocks are being seriously affected not so much by periodic outbreaks of disease, but by extensive illegal netting which prevents mature fish from reaching their spawning grounds. Invariably salmon return to rivers where they were hatched and it is obvious what damage can be done to stocks when large scale poaching takes place.

Spawning occurs during November or December. The eggs hatch in early spring and the young fish are called 'alevins'. As the yolk sac is absorbed and they emerge from the gravel bed where they hatched, they become known as 'fry'. The following year they are called 'parr'. After a period of two to four years in the river, they depart in late spring, at which stage they are known as 'smolts'. The young salmon then spend at least one year at sea and on its return it is called a 'grilse'.

Adults return to the river to spawn in the autumn. Salmon fresh from the sea can be identified by the presence of small parasites, which are known as sea lice, that are unable to survive in fresh water.

After spawning, the fish attempt to return to the sea. A large proportion are too weak to get there, being in such poor condition. At this stage they are known as 'kelts'.

Methods of Fishing

Rules for fishing vary from river to river. On many, only fly fishing is allowed; where exceptions are made, natural or spoon baits or spinners are permitted. A spinner is usually shaped like a fish, its fins causing it to spin with the pressure of the water. Spoon baits are designed to wobble, rather than spin underwater.

Salmon do not normally feed in fresh waters, so the flies used are designed as a lure rather than an imitation of any particular insect.

Fishing may be let by the rod, the day, week, month or year. Very often on large, wide rivers, fishing is not only conducted from the banks, but from boats as well.

Trout Management

For the river keeper on a recognised trout stream, care of the river is of prime importance. A great deal of time is spent in mowing the river banks, trimming the weed in the river and cutting back overhanging branches. Weed cutting is of importance in creating an environment that will prove attractive to fish and make fishing possible.

During the spring and summer, the banks are mowed weekly. Fringe growths of vegetation are trimmed to waist height. The actual weed in the river is cut once a month. It is trimmed back to approximately a foot beneath the surface and into a fan shape to provide an attractive area for the larval stage of insects. A pre-season cut is done in March, and a tidy up for the winter in October when the fringe vegetation is also cut back to ground level.

Weed cutting is done either by hand using a scythe, or a chain scythe worked by two people on either side of the river. The work is strenuous, as it may necessitate working waist deep in water in a strong current. Specially designed shallow boats equipped with cutters are also used. Nitrates washed into the river from surrounding farmland speed up the growth of water plants. Certain free-growing species are removed as they would soon smother beneficial slower growing varieties.

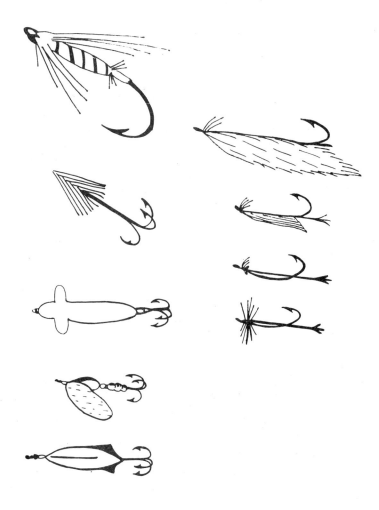

VARIOUS TYPES OF FLIES AND LURES

13.2 Shallow boats (here shown on a trailer) are sometimes used for reed cutting. Reciprocating blades (covered) are mounted at the front.

13.3 Pike can cause serious losses to fish and ducklings. The one illustrated weighed 16.25lbs and had swallowed the 1.25lb rudd laid beneath it.

Courtesy: Mr. M. Wingrove

By mutual agreement, certain days are set aside for weed cutting, when the debris is allowed to float down the river and be collected on booms operated by the river authorities. By this arrangement, no undue interference is caused to those fishing the lower stretches of the river. Booms are sometimes operated by individual owners.

River keepers work in close association with the river authorities by making regular checks on the water for pollution and noting possible water extraction.

Everything possible is done to encourage trout to breed successfully. Silt is cleared from the river beds to keep the gravel bottoms clear. Sometimes supplementary feed in the form of pellets will be fed to trout prior to, and after, spawning. This builds up condition and thus helps to counteract disease. Another practice is to fasten flat boards to an overhead branch. These float on the water surface and provide an excellent area on which insects will lay their eggs and on which, in turn, the trout will feed.

Treatment of diseased fish is virtually impossible in a river, but an attempt should be made to remove any that are affected. Three common diseases may be noted - FORUNCULOSIS - which is a fungal infection; U.D.N. - ulcerated derma neurosis, and I.P.N. - infectious pancratic neurosis. This latter disease only affects small fish, but survivors may act as carriers.

Predator Control

As well as providing the desirable habitat, the control of predators is equally important. Birds and other species of fish need to be dealt with. Electro fishing is usually conducted in the spring and autumn. This involves passing an electric current through the water, which alters the pulse rate to the brain, causing the fish to surface immediately. Recovery takes only a minute, although larger fish are affected more than small ones. Progress is made working upstream. The required species are left behind, while unwanted species are removed.

Eels, pike, roach and perch will devour both eggs and freshly hatched fry. These can all be removed by electro fishing.

Pike can often be observed lying in the river and can be removed by hand, using a rabbit snare attached to a pole.

Eels are trapped at night from mid-summer until Christmas. In many rivers, traps are built into the river, but smaller ones can be purchased. The darker the night the better to catch eels and it may be necessary to be up all night to supervise the operation.

On certain trout streams grayling numbers are also controlled.

13.4 A Hampshire trout river. The banks are kept mowed and the fringe vegetation is maintained at waist height.

Moorhens and coots can be troublesome to river keepers and their numbers need to be controlled. Other species such as swans, herons, cormorants and mergansers can be a nuisance and their presence is discouraged. Ducks are less harmful and arranging winter flighting may be included in a river keeper's duties.

Mink can play havoc on a river and every effort must be made to eliminate this harmful predator.

Poaching

Poachers are an ever-present problem and a careful watch must be kept at all times. A keen eye is needed to detect night lines that may have been placed beneath bridges or other shady places. The use of rods, nets and poison are other poaching methods employed and constant vigilance is required.

Some river keepers are endowed with special warrants to apprehend suspects. These are issued by the local police authority.

Etiquette

Individual rivers each have their sets of rules regarding the use of flies, baits, etc. Some of the select trout streams only permit the use of a dry fly or a nymph floated on the water. On such rivers it is etiquette to face and cast upstream only; to transgress the rules is a cardinal sin. The extreme of using barbless hooks has even reached some rivers, the fishermen being content with outwitting their fish and not wishing it any harm.

It is the river keeper's job to ensure that these rules are not broken. Much of his time will be spent walking around and observing. His advice of choice of fly and hook will frequently be asked for. His duty is to assist others to enjoy their sport and he may even be called upon to cook lunch!!

Trout Fishing

The subject of attracting fish actually onto a hook is extensive, to say the least. Whilst the use of spinners, natural baits, etc. is comparatively straightforward, the art of fly fishing is anything but. With a choice from many thousands of different flies, each one individually named, the topic is limitless. Familiarity with the selection of flies and a knowledge of fly tying is a necessary part of a river keeper's job.

The word 'fly' is a loose term that covers an imitation of any insect, or different stage of insect development, that a fish may feed on. Extremely careful observation is needed to identify what species is proving attractive at any particular place or time.

13.5 Competitions are often arranged to test the skill of the fly fisher.

13.6 Salmon do not feed in fresh water. The flies used are large and often brightly coloured to attract the attention of the fish.

The best-known fly to trout fishermen is undoubtedly the may fly. When, at a certain time, usually during May, they hatch in vast numbers, and hungry trout will gorge themselves. This is commonly known in fishing circles as 'duffers fortnight', when the fishing is easy. However, after this period, when the trout have satisfied their appetite, they will prove much harder to catch.

Trout can be extremely selective in what they will take, even so far as selecting the female of the species in preference to a male. Occasionally one will lie up beneath an overhanging tree and will feed on bugs or even lady birds that fall into the water.

When a trout has been caught and landed, the contents of the stomach should be examined to determine what species of insect the trout has been feeding on. An elongated spoon, originally designed for removing marrow from within a bone, and called a marrow spoon for that reason, is ideal for the purpose.

Life cycle of water insects

Trout eat insects at all different stages of development. Water temperature triggers off the hatching of the insect eggs. In the case of the may fly, this occurs usually in May. The larvae change into what is known as a nymph. These may live for a year or more on the river bottom before rising to the surface. The freshly hatched insect is called a 'dun'. It floats on the surface before flying or crawling out onto the nearby foliage. Here, it dries for up to forty eight hours, a process that is completed in the evening when it becomes known as a 'spinner'. These can be seen dancing above the water on a calm evening. They mate in the air and the female will either crawl or dive-bomb into the water to lay her eggs. After this, both sexes die and can be seen floating on the water. At this stage they are called 'spent spinners'.

Other common species on southern chalk streams are sedge (cadis) flies, olives and iron blues.

The sedge fly build themselves a tube of stones, sand, etc. underwater at the nymph stage and may lay dormant for several years. They hatch throughout the year, but usually in late evening, and they return to the water.

Olives also hatch throughout the year and are very prolific in the summer. Colours vary from dark, medium and light.

Iron blue are a steel blue in colour and generally hatch after a shower of rain.

Trout that can be seen feeding just beneath the surface will be feeding on nymphs.

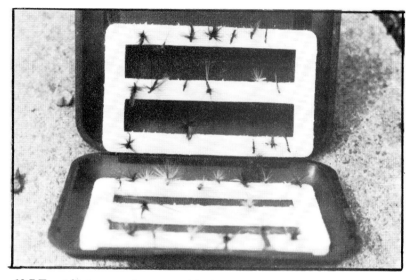

13.7 Trout flies are made to resemble the insects that the fish are feeding on.

13.8 The freshly hatched insect is called a dun. It flies or crawls onto nearby foliage where it dries for up to 48 hours.

Flies

A 'fly' is an imitation of one particular insect made up from fur and feathers, and sometimes tinsel. Slivers of the chosen material are bound onto a hook to represent the required species. Sometimes they are incorporated onto treble hooks. Flies for trout fishing are often very small, while salmon flies are somewhat larger and more gaudy. The treble hooked flies are only used to catch salmon or sea trout.

Fish Hatching

On some rivers hatcheries are operated where rainbow and brown trout are bred and reared. Usually this is a commercial concern to supply still water fisheries or the table requirements. However, a few brown trout may be released into the river. Rainbow are regarded with disdain by the dedicated fisherman.

Rainbows are commercially more successful than browns, as they grow twice as quickly and are half as much trouble to rear.

Stock fish, known as 'cocks' and 'hens', are selected for size and growth rate. The eggs are manually stripped from the hen fish in October and fertilised with milt, stripped from the cock fish. This is of necessity cold work. If the hands are warm, injury can be caused to the stock fish during handling.

These fertilised eggs are placed into special indoor tanks, where they develop. Hatching commences about Christmas time. The tanks are flat and about eighteen inches 45 cms.) deep. The tiny fry are black in colour. Rainbows prefer to gather near the surface, while browns stay near to the bottom of the tank. The water in the tanks needs to be warmer than the river water and is often extracted from springs. It is continuously bubbled through the tanks.

The yolk sac provides sufficient nourishment for the young fry until feeding commences at about eight days. A very high protein meal is dispensed automatically at frequent intervals.

In early summer, when the water temperature outside is high enough, the fry are counted and transferred to outside rearing tanks. Counting is carried out by lifting the individual fry out of the tanks by using a feather.

The outdoor tanks are called 'stews' and a series of tanks will hold trout at different stages of growth. To begin with a fine mesh netting will be needed to give protection from kingfishers. At a later stage a larger mesh netting will be required as a defence from the attentions of herons who can cause serious losses.

The trout are fed high protein rations during this time, and grow very quickly and become very tame. They are selected for sale throughout the summer, either for the table or restocking. The most popular weight is from one to one and a half pounds.

Trout required at a larger size are moved into more roomy tanks for a further period.

The artificial rearing of salmon and sea trout is still in the experimental stages, but is quickly becoming of commercial interest.

13.9 Stew ponds protected from Kingfishers and Herons by nets

Courtesy: P. Mitchener

14
DEER CONTROL

Reading on Wild Deer:
Stag Hunting on Exmoor by M.C. McGowan
(Nimrod Press)

14.1 Sika stag with antlers in velvet.

14.2 Fallow Deer.

Seasons

A close season from 1 March - 31 October has been proposed for Muntjac and Chinese Water Deer - both sexes.

Close Seasons for Deer (Dates inclusive)

		ENGLAND & WALES	SCOTLAND
RED	Stags	1 May - 31 July	21 Oct. - 30 June
	Hinds	1 March - 31 Oct.	16 Feb. - 20 Oct.
FALLOW	Buck	1 May - 31 July	1 May - 31 July
	Doe	1 March - 31 Oct.	16 Feb. - 20 October
ROE	Buck	1 Nov. - 31 March	21 Oct. - 31 March
	Doe	1 March - 31 Oct.	1 April - 20 October
SIKA	Stags	1 May - 31 July	21 Oct. - 30 June
	Hinds	1 March - 31 Oct.	16 Feb. - 20 October
RED/SIKA	Stags		21 Oct. - 30 June
HYBRIDS	Hinds		16 Feb. - 20 Oct.

Responsibilities of the Keeper

Deer control sometimes falls in the hands of the keeper, but more often than not it is let to paying individuals. Even when not directly involved with the control, the services of the keeper are often required to collect a carcase or to search for a wounded beast with his dog. The keeper may be expected to gut and skin the beast and to prepare the head as a trophy. The knowledge of the whereabouts of deer, whether carrying a quality head or that need culling, is appreciated by stalkers.

The keeper on his rounds should keep watch for deer that have been crippled by road accidents, etc. These can then be culled as soon as possible.

14.3 Roe Deer.

14.4 Red Deer (above) spend most of the year in herds of separate sexes, as do Fallow and Sika. Roe, Chinese Water Deer and Muntjac stay in family groups.

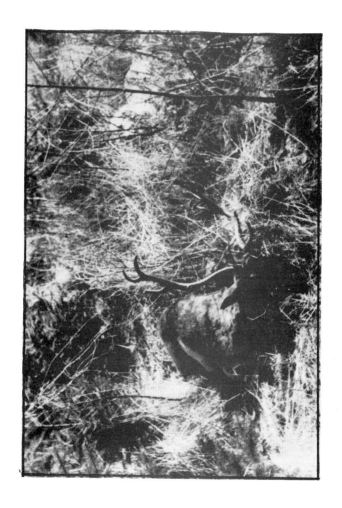

14.5 A dog may sometimes be needed to find a wounded deer.

Signs of poaching such as illegal use of lurchers or snares, must also be watched for.

Stalking is usually let by the value of the head or per doe or hind that is culled. The stalker should always inform the keeper or other fellow stalkers of his intended whereabouts.

Species

There are six species of deer to be found living wild in Great Britain. Red, Fallow, Roe, Sika, Muntjac and Chinese Water Deer. The latter two are escapees from parks that are found locally, but have now established themselves and are increasing their range away from the original location.

Red Deer are distributed mainly in the highlands of Scotland, where the letting of stalking provides a much needed income on otherwise unprofitable ground. They are usually found in wild, hilly regions, although red deer also frequent forestry and farmland where they may cause considerable damage to crops. Reds are the largest British deer and stand up to four feet (122 cms.) at the shoulder. They are highly regarded by sportsmen; a large spread of antlers with many points is an esteemed trophy. Stalking may involve many hours of creeping and crawling across rocky terrain to get into a suitable shooting position. Deer are very keen sighted and possess an excellent sense of smell; they are wary creatures and the approach needs to be made with the utmost caution.

Hinds are culled during the winter to control numbers, but there is not the glamour attached to shooting hinds that there is to shooting stags.

The heavy carcases may be difficult to remove from such a wilderness and it may be necessary to drag it to a place where a vehicle or a pony may be taken to collect it.

The mating season is during the autumn; this is known as the rut. At this time, stags can be heard 'roaring' as they lay claim to the hinds. The young are born in May or June and they are dappled in colour.

A few herds of red deer exist in parks and deer farming for venison is becoming a profitable enterprise in some areas.

Fallow Deer enjoy a more mixed habitat, preferring woodland and farmland. Many herds are kept in parks of stately homes. Their colouring ranges from almost black through to pure white, but the most common colour is sandy, with white dapples, changing to a darker shade in the winter. The antlers are flatter than the other species of deer and the tail, which is constantly flicked

RED STAG
14 points is called a Monarch
12 points is called a Royal

SIKA STAG

FALLOW BUCK

ROE BUCK

MUNTJAC BUCK

DIAGRAM OF ANTLER STRUCTURE (not to scale).

Chinese water deer have no antlers.

14.6 Muntjac deer showing peculiar bone formation of the antlers which starts between the nose and the eye.

14.7 Muntjac have small antlers and upper canine teeth that grow like tusks.

from side to side, is longer. Fallow are smaller than the red, standing up to three feet six inches (107 cms.) at the shoulder. The rut is also in the autumn, and the young are born during May or June.

Roe Deer are shy creatures that prefer woodland and forestry. They are reddish brown in summer, changing to a mousy brown in winter. They have increased rapidly during recent years, due, no doubt in part, to the increase of fir plantations, a favoured haunt. Numbers need to be controlled, as extensive damage may be caused to young trees by browsing, and bucks using their antlers. The latter occurs during the marking out of territories and, to some extent, from the efforts of removing the velvet from newly formed antlers. The rut is usually at the end of July and early August, but the young are not born until the following May. The extended pregnancy is due to a delayed development of the foetus. Unlike red and fallow deer, the roe does not live in herds, but stays in smaller family units. Another difference occurs in that red and fallow commonly have only one calf or fawn, but roe frequently have two and occasionally three. At a distance, there is no visible sign of a tail and, when disturbed, a roe deer will bark like a dog. The young fawns are often left hidden and occasionally are killed or maimed by farm machinery cutting crops they are concealed in.

Sika Deer (Japanese) have become naturalised in the British Isles during the last century. They are closely related to red deer and have similar shaped antlers, although in size and colouring they resemble fallow. In Scotland they are popular for stalking, as they offer an opportunity in areas that are favoured by neither red nor roe. The rut is in the autumn and the young are born during May or June. Occasionally cross breeding occurs with red deer.

Muntjac Deer have recently been extending their range since escaping from Woburn Park in Bedfordshire earlier this century. They are small creatures, little bigger than a fox and, like roe, live in family groups. The bucks have very small antlers and visible canine teeth which look like tusks. They apparently have no fixed breeding season. Their bark can be mistaken for that of a fox.

Chinese Water Deer are another species that is gradually establishing itself in the wild, having escaped from parks. They are slightly larger than Muntjac. The males grow tusks, but have no antlers. The rut occurs during November and the females may give birth to as many as six young during May or June.

14.8 Deer Stalking.

HIGH SEAT FOR VIEWING

Free standing high seats are often sited in open clearings or newly planted woodland and are constructed from locally grown timber.

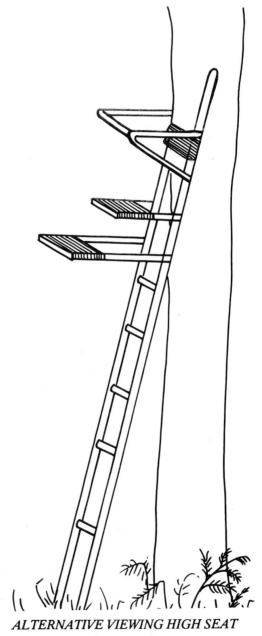

ALTERNATIVE VIEWING HIGH SEAT

Metal high seats are movable. They can be secured to a tree to give a good view of a ride, clearing, or across fields.

Facts about deer

Nearly all species of deer have white rumps which act as a danger or recognition signal. The males cast their antlers and grow new ones each year which are covered in a sensitive skin called 'velvet'. This is removed by rubbing against trees, etc., and may be seen hanging from the antlers in strips. The young are nearly always born with a dappled coat which provides an excellent camouflage when they are left unattended. They will stay in one place for many hours and, if discovered, should be left undisturbed as the dam will not be far away.

The control of deer numbers is necessary to prevent excessive damage to forestry and crops, and to keep the population at a level that the ground can support. The shooting of stags or bucks can be let to provide an additional income for the estate. Trophy heads are much prized by stalkers, and are graded on an international scale into gold, silver or bronze medal standards. Weight, size and appearance are taken into consideration. The culling of inferior stags or bucks and hinds or does also provides income both from the letting of the stalking and the value of the carcases.

Deer come out of cover to feed during early morning and late evening, which is the best time for stalking.

Stalking

Many ploys are used to shoot deer other than stalking. High seats are often erected in trees that offer a clear view in wooded areas. The stalker can wait undetected for the deer to cross the clearings beneath him. Calling deer by imitating the cries of adults or their young can also be effective in luring a beast within killing range, especially during the rut.

It is illegal to snare or trap deer or to shoot from a vehicle. It is no longer legal to use a shotgun, except in certain circumstances for crop protection (see Chapter 18). Not many years ago, deer drives were arranged when beaters drove deer towards waiting guns with shotguns. This practice is now illegal. There is a specific calibre of rifle that can be used for any species of deer. A minimum .240 is required and bullets must be soft-nosed or hollow-nosed.

Certain exceptions may be made for killing deer during the close season when crop damage occurs, in which case an S.16 licence must be obtained. Legislation concerning deer is dealt with in Chapter 18.

Knowledge of the area is important when stalking, and the safety of the shot a prime consideration. A rifle bullet, if it misses its target, can travel a great distance. The selected deer should be clearly visible and stationery.

Opinions differ as to which part of the body should be aimed at. Some stalkers prefer the head or neck, assuming that with a small target it should either be a case of a hit or a clean miss. However, if the bullet hits the animal, but fails to kill, the deer may be so injured that it dies a lingering death, such as if the jaw is broken. Other stalkers prefer a heart shot, as this offers a larger target area and, even if not absolutely accurate, the bullet should prove fatal. Slight inaccuracy, however, may cause the bullet to deflect off the bone and even an accurate heart shot may result in the deer running up to a hundred yards before dropping. Obviously this may make locating the animal very difficult in thick cover. At a time such as this, a good dog will prove useful. The bullet used must be soft- or hollow-nosed to have the maximum effect. The stalker should be familiar with shooting from either the standing, sitting or prone position.

There are several items of equipment that it is necessary to take on a stalking expedition. The appropriate rifle should be fitted with a telescopic sight and must have been previously zeroed in on a target, to ensure accuracy. Binoculars are required to select a suitable individual when deer are located. A sharp knife will be needed to grallock the deer as soon as possible after it is shot. The liver and kidneys may be retained. Spare ammunition should be carried, as there is always a possibility that more than one shot will be needed to kill the beast.

Other useful items are a torch, a strong stick on which to steady the rifle, and some sort of bag or harness for carrying the smaller species of deer.

The Stalker's dog

A well trained dog is an extremely useful asset to own when stalking in thick cover. A wounded deer need only travel a few yards in thick undergrowth before it is lost from sight. Any breed of dog may be used and the choice ranges from terrier to G.S.P. But it must be quiet and obedient; if it will bark when locating a wounded deer, so much the better. If a dog is to be trained specifically for deer stalking, it must be taught to track a blood scent and either bay at the deer or return to its handler and lead him back to the animal. The dog must also, of course, be steady to fur and feather, walk to heel, and be trained to stay quiet where it is left for long periods.

Hill Stalking

Hill stalking is an arduous sport, and the stalker needs to be physically fit. As in woodland stalking, great attention must be paid to the direction of the wind. The slightest whiff of human scent will send wild deer away at a run and many hours of patient stalking will be wasted. Suitable well camouflaged clothing must be worn and a compass may prove very useful if mists descend or darkness falls quickly.

Preparation of the Trophy Head

The carcase is best hung up to skin. The head is often prepared for mounting on a wooden shield by the following method. As soon as possible, as much skin and flesh should be removed. The head should then be laid on its side and sawn in half on a line from the back of the skull, through the centre of the eye sockets, to the tip of the nostrils. This should then be boiled in water, to which a handful of soda crystals have been added, until all the flesh can be cleaned from the bones. The bone part only should then be soaked in hydrogen peroxide (Domestic solution) to bleach it white before being mounted on the shield. Frequently the jaw bones containing the teeth are saved to provide information such as age.

The antlers a stag or buck carry increase in size annually and it may be several years before they reach maximum development. However, after a peak has been reached, and the animal grows older and past its prime, the antler growth deteriorates each year.

14.9 A Gold Medal trophy head of a roe buck mounted on a wooden shield.

14.9 The dappled coat of young deer provides excellent camouflage.

(Young Roe shown)

15
Firearms

Recommended reading:
Shotgun Shooting - Techniques and Technology
by Dr. John Brindle

I should like to thank Mr. Jim Sims of Twyford, Winchester, Hants for his assistance when writing this chapter. My thanks, also, extend to Gunmark Ltd., Fareham, Hants for photographs and Eley Ltd., P.O. Box 216, Wilton, Birmingham, for illustrations and data.

15.1 Cabinet for storing guns (essential for security reasons)

(Courtesy Patrick Pinker (Game Farm) Ltd.)

Firearms

Shotguns

A certificate is required to be in possession of a shotgun and an application form is available from the local Police Station.

Firearms (Rifle)

Strict regulations are enforced concerning the possession of a rifle and ammunition. Application for a certificate must be made in the first instance to the local police station from where it will be forwarded to County Headquarters.

Air Rifle

No licence is required unless it exceeds a specified power output, in which case a Firearms Certificate is necessary.

Legislation concerning shotguns, rifles and air rifles is dealt with in Chapter 18.

Notes on Gun Safety

A gun of any type should never be pointed at anyone. The safety catch should not be released until the moment prior to firing.

A gun should always be unloaded before climbing fences, crossing difficult areas, standing or laying it down, when handing it to another person or at any time when it may be a danger to the user or any other person in the vicinity.

Never attempt to shoot when in an unstable position or with a dog tied to your person.

Always check it is safe to shoot, take into account the area surrounding the target. This is especially important when using a rifle, when the bullet may travel in excess of a mile.

Damage to any part of the gun must be avoided at all times as this may render it unsafe. The barrels of a shotgun should be inspected immediately if there is any possibility that they may have become blocked.

Guns and cartridges should be stored in a secure place.

Rifles are legally required to be kept iun a locked cabinet, preferably steel.

Serial numbers of all guns possessed should be noted.

The gun must be checked that it is unloaded before it is brought indoors and storea away.

Children should never be allowed access to any guns unless they are constantly supervised.

Guns left in vehicles must be unloaded, kept out of sight and preferably stored in a slip. The vehicle must be locked when left unattended.

Never mix different size cartridges; a smaller bore may be accidentally placed in a larger size gun and become jammed inside the barrel.

New legislation concerning firearms may be introduced at any time so the latest regulations must be obtained.

Shotguns and Rifles

The subject of shotguns, rifles and ammunition is extensive, as various modifications and refinements are available. A brief summary should be adequate, and if further more specific information is required, then this can be obtained from the many specialised books there are available on the subject.

Providing a gun is nitro-proofed and in full working order and reliable ammunition is used, it is the person who pulls the trigger who determines whether the target is hit. A good shot will perform as well with a suitable gun costing £100 as he would with one costing £10,000.

The difference between a rifle and a shotgun, basically, is that a rifle fires a single shot or bullet for a long distance, and a shotgun fires a number of smaller shots a shorter distance.

Development of the modern firearm

The modern precision-made guns have developed over many centuries. In the thirteenth century an explosive mixture of sulphur, saltpetre and charcoal was invented and was called gun- or black- powder. The potential was soon realised and from that time, guns were continually improved.

The first guns were basic canons. Using a controlled explosion, they were used to fire stones, arrows or iron shot. Over the years they were developed to be small enough to be used by hand and were fitted with a match lock. This consisted of a piece of bent steel and a length of sulphur soaked burning

Left: .22 Air Rifle. Middle: .22 bolt action rifle with bullet and magazine. Right: .223 bolt action rifle with bullet.

All rifles illustrated are fitted with telescopic sights.

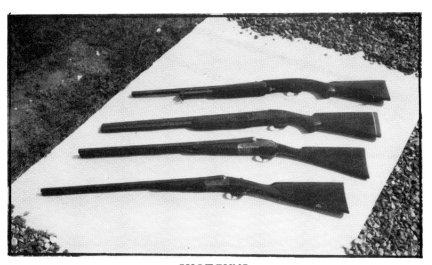

SHOTGUNS

Top: Pump action 12 bore. 2nd: Over and under 12 bore. 3rd: Side by side sidelock 12 bore. Bottom: Side by side box lock 28 bore.

15.2 Different types of guns

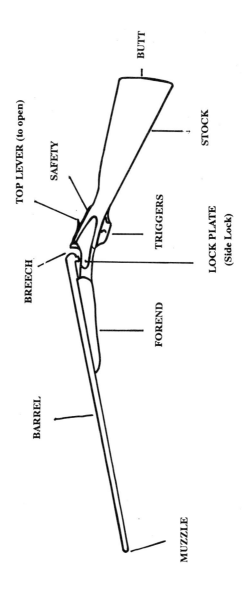

DIAGRAM OF A SHOTGUN

string. When the trigger was pulled, the string was automaticcally lowered into a touch hole containing gunpowder and the gun went off.

Continued development saw the invention of the flintlock. A more elaborate mechanism whereby a hammer held a flint which, when released, made contact with a piece of steel causing a spark. This, in turn, went into a touch hole, thus firing the gun.

Further refinements came about with the invention of the percussion lock. This replaced the flint with a cup, which fitted over a small hollow tube. Onto the end of this was fitted a percussion cap similar to the cap at the centre of a modern cartridge; when the hammer was cocked and fired, this sent a spark down into the charge of powder. Until this time all guns had been muzzle loaded; that is, the powder wadding and shot were rammed into position through the muzzle end of the barrel. After each shot had been fired the procedure was repeated.

The breach loading gun was invented in the mid-nineteenth century and drastically altered every aspect of shooting.

Cartridges were produced that already contained the necessary percussion cap, powder, wadding and shot. The new design of gun opened in the middle and the cartridges were easily and quickly inserted into place. The cartridge cases were made out of paper and the firing mechanism was still worked by hammers. The whole process was speeded up. Until this time it had only been practical to shoot at quarry that was motionless or slow moving. With the invention of this faster reloading process, shooting birds in flight became possible, resulting in game being driven towards standing guns by beaters.

Continued refinements were made to incorporate the firing mechanism inside the gun and a safety catch was added. This pattern of gun was called a hammerless breech loader.

The final major development was the addition of a device that would eject spent cartridges, thus making the process of reloading even faster.

Advances continue in design and improvements are being made to increase accuracy and ease of handling.

The modern Shotgun

Modern shotguns are manufactured with either one barrel or two. These are either placed side by side, or one above the other, in which case it is known as an over and under.

Shotguns are produced in the following sizes, beginning with the smallest : .410, 28.20.16.12.10.8 and 4 bore. The killing range varies according to the size of gun and the type of shot used. A .410 may be approximately twenty five yards, and a 12 bore may be forty yards.

With the exception of the .410, the bore was originally determined by the number of lead balls, adding up to 16 ounces in weight, that would fit into the gun, e.g.: 12 balls equalled 16 ounces for a 12 bore and 28 balls for a 28 bore. Thus the bore denotes the size of the barrel.

The .410, however, is the measurement of the diameter in thousandths of an inch.

Barrels

Originally barrels were made the same size at both ends, which caused the shot to spread rapidly when it left the gun. In 1874 a gunsmith by the name of Greener discovered that if the last few inches of the muzzle end were slightly tapered, the shot held together in a better pattern. However, more than a fraction of an inch caused the shot to scatter even more. This tapering was known as 'choke' and greatly improved the capabilities of the shotgun as a killing weapon.

The chokes were developed and the improvement made to shot patterns can be seen from the table below. The restriction is measured in thousandths of an inch, the range is forty yards, and the percentage is that of pellets in a 30 inch circle.

True cylinder		40%
Improved cylinder	$\frac{3.5}{1000}$	50%
1/4 choke	$\frac{10}{1000}$	55%
1/2 choke	$\frac{20}{1000}$	60%
3/4 choke	$\frac{30}{1000}$	65%

Full choke   40   70%

                          1000

Conventional side by side shotguns normally have different chokes in each barrel. When the front of the two triggers is pulled the right hand barrel is fired and this is usually improved cylinder, 1/4 choke or 1/2 choke. The back trigger fires the left hand barrel which is most likely to be 3/4 or full choke. The reason for this design is because when the second barrel is fired, it is most likely to be at a target that is going away. Therefore, by selecting the barrel with a tighter choke, the shot will hold together more and be accurate at a greater distance.

The length of barrel is a matter of personal choice. The legal minimum is 24 inches. There is no maximum length, but usually barrel length does not exceed 32 inches although some of the large bore guns may be longer.

A popular choice of shotgun is a 12 bore with 28 inch barrels and half and full chokes. A side by side is the usual choice for game shooting and an over and under for clay shooting.

Cartridges

Cartridge cases are made from either paper or plastic. At the base is a metal part that contains a percussion cap known as a primer. On top of this inside is the powder - no longer black powder, but a nitro compound. Above this comes the wadding made either from paper or plastic. Lastly comes the shot and the top of the cartridge is crimped over to secure the shot inside. See page 260.

There is a wide choice of shot size contained within the cartridge, ranging from LG which constitutes 6 pellets per ounce (2 per 10 grams) down to No. 9 shot, constituting 580 pellets per ounce.

Normally Nos. 5, 6 or 7 are used for game shooting and the heavier shots used for wildfowl, hare, foxes, etc.

Sizes of shot larger than No. 1 (100 pellets per ounce) is known as lettered shot. Full details are given on page 263.

Lengths of cartridges for a typical 12 bore vary from 2 inches to 3 inches, but care must be taken to make sure that the chambers of the barrel in which the cartridges are inserted are long enough to house the chosen size.

The weight of pellets inside the cartridges is also a matter of personal choice. A .410 cartridge may contain as little as 5/16 of an ounce, and a 3 inch 12 bore cartridge as much as 1 7/8 of an ounce.

The usual choice for a 2 1/2 inch chambered 12 bore falls between 1 and 1 3/16 ounces.

Design

The lock of a gun houses the firing mechanism and designs vary slightly. There are two standards: the box lock and the side lock. The latter has the external plates along the sides extended towards the stock, is the better quality action, and is often beautifully engraved.

Stocks vary in length and should be selected to fit comfortably into the shoulder. If the gun is used frequently, the stock should be measured and fitted to suit the individual. Shortening of the stock will require the services of an experienced gun smith. Lengthening can sometimes be satisfactorily achieved by the fitting of a recoil pad to the butt.

Modifications are made to shotguns to suit personal comfort and nearly every part of a shotgun can be altered.

Interchangeable choke tubes are now manufactured to allow for a complete range of choke to fit one gun.

There are many variations to the basic design of the shotgun which are marketed. One example which is particularly popular in the United States and Canada is the double barrelled shotgun with a single trigger. When hunters are working in arctic conditions and need to wear thick gloves, the use of a single trigger eliminates the difficulty of selecting separate triggers.

Shotguns, apart from size, are divided into different categories. There are single barrelled which fire only one cartridge at a time, there are double barrelled, either side by side or over and under, that can be loaded with two cartridges; and there are semi-automatics and pump actions which can take up to eight cartridges.

Semi-Automatic Shotguns

If these are used for game shooting it is a legal requirement that the semi-automatics are blanked off so that they are limited to holding three cartridges.

The magazine holding the cartridges is usually incorporated in the forend beneath the barrel and the cartridges are inserted into the breach automatically.

Various methods of automatic loading have been devised, including the following :

Recoil operated

The barrel recoils on firing, ejecting the empty case and forcing the new cartridge into the breach.

Gas operated

A hole in the barrel leads to a non-return valve. Gas from the fired cartridge is forced through the hole and into the valve from where it blows into the breach mechanism. The barrels themselves remain stationery as the gas is used to eject the empty case and force the fresh cartridge into the breach.

Manually operated

The methods used are: pump or lever actions. The pump action shotgun is reloaded by sliding the forend and the lever action by an exaggerated trigger guard which is pulled down.

Choice of shotgun

Selection of the appropriate shotgun may at first seem difficult, with such a wide range to choose from. However, the size and design should be governed by the use for which the gun is intended. The smaller range of bores are usually chosen by the young or the elderly as they provide a lighter weapon. Larger bores are the choice of wildfowlers where the quarry is larger and often more distant. Over and unders are favoured by clay shooters and side by sides preferred by game shooters. Although both are suitable for either function, a slight prejudice still exists in shooting circles over the use of an over and under for game.

When everything is taken into consideration, it is usually found that the 12 bore is the most suitable all-rounder, with the 20 bore the runner-up.

Maintenance

Maintenance of the shotgun must be carefully attended to, especially if it has been used during wet weather or it is likely to be stored for a while.

After use, the forend should be removed and the barrels unclipped. The separate parts should be dried. The barrels should be cleaned by first pushing toilet or other soft paper through from the breach end, to remove excess dirt. Some mineral oil should be put inside the barrels and scrubbed round with a phosphor bronze brush attached to a cleaning rod. The dirt should once again be removed with soft paper or cloth. A final light oiling should be given on a wool mop fixed to the cleaning rod, but excessive oiling should be avoided. This can cause damage in two ways. Firstly, by causing an obstruction within the barrel which may result in rippling when fired; and, secondly, if the mineral oil drains onto the wood of the stock or forend and is allowed to penetrate, it will break down the fibres of the wood. The exterior of the barrels should also be given a very light oiling.

The face of the breach and around the firing pins should be wiped over with a lightly oiled cloth and any dirt removed from behind the extractors.

The woodwork should be cleaned with a dry cloth and a small amount of linseed oil rubbed into it with the palm of the hand.

The gun should then be reassembled. It is best stored in a constant temperature and preferably not in a slip. Temperature fluctuations will cause the metal to sweat and rust will soon become apparent. Vinyl gun slips may also cause a gun to rust, and great care must be taken too that sheepskin slips are thoroughly dried before the gun is stored inside. The slightest amount of moisture present will induce rust, which will quickly eat through the metal.

Modern cartridges keep shotguns in good condition with the minimum amount of attention. Obviously any repairs that are necessary should be made as soon as possible. A dent in a barrel can soon wear through and explode if the gun is used frequently. Triggers, too, should be kept in good order and adjusted when necessary. A shotgun that is not kept in good repair can be a very dangerous weapon and every attention should be paid with regard to safety at all times.

See chapter 18 for legislation concerning the shotgun.

Loading

Many keepers are expected to load when their employers shoot double guns. It is very important to know how to do this correctly in order that the operation is conducted smoothly, quickly and safely.

It is very difficult for a right-handed person to load for a left-handed one, or vice versa.

Presuming that both 'gun' and loader are right-handed, the loader should position himself just behind the 'gun's' right hand shoulder and facing in the same direction. The gun he is holding should be in his right hand with the muzzles pointing upwards.

When either one, or both, barrels have been fired by his employer, the loader should take the discharged gun with the left hand gripping it round the forend and barrels. At the same time the loaded gun is passed to the left hand of the employer by being held round the narrowest part of the stock in the right hand.

When the exchange is completed, the loader should turn to the rear, well out of line of other guns, before lowering the barrels downwards. The empty cartridges or cartridge should be ejected and the gun reloaded and closed. The gun should be returned to its position of readiness before the loader turns back to face the drive.

The basic technique for both loader and gun is to take with the left hand gripping the forend and to pass with the right hand holding the small of the stock.

At all times the gun must be on safe and if the employer is negligent about this, the loader should remind him.

An experienced loader can hold several cartridges between his fingers ready for instant reloading. A roomy cartridge bag is also required to increase the speed of loading. When a flush of birds is overhead a 'gun' will expect to be able to fire at least four barrels at it, so speed is essential.

It is beneficial to have a practice session beforehand with empty guns to adjust to working in unison.

A useful tool to possess is a cartridge extractor - a simple device that quickly removes a cartridge case from the breech if it has got jammed. Failing this a pocket knife will prove adequate if needed.

The loader will be responsible for carrying the guns, cartridges and other items. It is also his responsibility to ensure that sufficient cartridges are available for each drive. An employer is never very pleased if the cartridges run out before the drive has ended, particularly if he is in the hot spot!

The keeper must also be aware of the value of his employer's guns, many of which have been handed from father to son. Great care must be taken that the guns are never knocked against each other during exchange. Barrels are very easily dented and repairs will deprive the 'gun' of one of his pair for many weeks.

It is a wise precaution, when carrying guns in slips, to have the barrels pointing downwards. The loader will, of course, have checked that they are not loaded, but by carrying them barrel downwards, there is no risk of them sliding out of an insecurely fastened slip.

Serious permanent damage can be caused to the hearing when loading and shooting. It is therefore recommended that ear protectors should be worn.

The Rifle

Originally, rifles were smooth bored like shotguns, but improvements have added the refinement of a corkscrew spiral projection of the single bullet. This is brought about by incorporating 'lands' and 'grooves' inside the barrel.

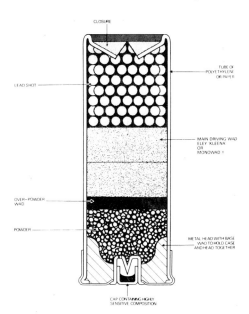

DIAGRAM OF AN ELEY CARTRIDGE

When the bullet is fired, it is forced into the 'lands', forming a seal so that no gas escapes backwards. All the energy is spent in forcing the bullet through the barrel to send it spiralling out. The 'lands' themselves may only be two one thousandths of an inch deep. Although it is a highly technical subject, for example, in modern centre fire rifles there is one rotation in 16 inches for a .22 rifle and one in 12 inches for a .243. Any increase in the number of turns inside the barrel would cause the bullet to strip.

The most common rifle calibres are .22, Hornet, .222, .240, .243, .270 and .308. Sizes below the .240 can only be used on small vermin in England, but can be used for roe deer in Scotland. The larger sizes are used for shooting deer. Commonly the .243 is used for roe deer and the .270 and . 308 for red, sika or fallow. Automatics are frowned upon and the bolt action single shot with a box or clip-on magazine is recommended.

Ammunition can be loaded automatically with the use of magazines which either clip above or below the breech of a bolt action rifle. The bullets are loaded into these box magazines laying lengthways, one above the other. They are forced lengthways into the breech by a spring when a spent cartridge is ejected.

Tubular magazines are fitted either into the forend or into the stock, in which case they are loaded from the butt end. This type of magazine stores the bullets nose to tail and, for this reason, pointed bullets should not be used. A spring pushes the bullets forward and there is an obvious danger if the pointed nose of one bullet is pushed up tight against the primer of the one in front. This is the method used for semi-automatic rifles.

On most smaller rifles the breech spring is made weak enough that the blow back action when fired ejects the spent case and allows another bullet to be forced into position.

Larger rifles are usually operated by a similar method to a gas operated shotgun. These may also be pump, bolt or lever action reloading.

Rifle bullets may actually be fired by two different methods. The centre fire is similar to a shotgun cartridge and the primer is in the centre of the base. The rim fire incorporates the primer in the rim of the base.

Ammunition

There are numerous different sizes and designs of bullets from which a selection may be made. The choice depends on which purpose and quarry it is intended and expert advice should be acquired to suit individual requirements. Some bullets travel faster than the speed of sound and some are hollow-nosed or soft pointed, which causes them to flatten and spread on impact. A .22 bullet carries the warning that it can be dangerous within one mile, therefore great care must be taken when selecting a target. Regard must be paid to what there is behind the quarry and, even if the target is hit, the bullet may pass right through and continue on its way.

Maintenance

Rifles require very little maintenance other than the obvious removal of dirt and moisture. Opinions differ as to whether any internal cleaning is necessary at all. Most modern ammunition is self-lubricating and, if the rifle is used regularly, the barrel will remain in perfect condition.

Telescopic sights

Telescopic sights are frequently fitted to rifles and care is needed not to knock these. It is imperative to get the sights lined up accurately on targets at a suitable range before any animals or birds are shot at. A single rifle bullet hits a comparatively small area of its target, therefore it is very important that the killing area selected, such as the head or the heart, is hit first time accurately.

Air Rifles

Air rifles use the energy from compressed air to propel the single lead pellet or slug from a similarly grooved barrel. Small darts are sometimes used for target practice.

Two calibres are manufactured, the .177 and the more powerful .22. A combination of modern technology and precision engineering has resulted in some powerful weapons being produced. As yet there is no legal requirement to hold a licence or a permit to own one, unless it exceeds a specified power output.

The Punt Gun

The punt gun is a very basic form of gun - a simple canon mounted in a flat boat.

Although of ancient design, it is still used around marshes and coastal areas today. Since the 1950s, the diameter of the barrel has been limited to 1 3/4 inches. Originally it was muzzle loading, but breech loading guns utilising a large pre-loaded cartridge are sometimes used in present times.

The punt on which the gun is mounted is usually operated by one man working silently and alone. The punt is manoeuvred within a range of 70 - 100 yards of wild fowl that are resting on or near water.

When within range, the gun is fired and, when the smoke has cleared, the punt gunner hopes to pick up several birds from the one shot

NUMBER OF PELLETS IN SHOT LOAD
(nominal)

Weight of Shot		Size of Shot					
g	oz	3	4	5	6	7	8
46	1.5/8	228	276	358	439	552	732
42.5	1.1/2	210	255	330	405	510	675
36	1.1/4	175	213	275	338	425	562
34	1.3/16	166	202	261	321	404	534
32	1.1/8	157	191	248	304	383	506
30	1.1/16	149	181	234	287	361	478
28.5	1	140	170	220	270	340	450
26.5	15/16	131	159	206	253	319	422
25	7/8	122	149	193	236	298	394
23	13/16	113	138	179	219	276	366
17.5	5/8	87	106	138	169	212	282
16	9/16	78	96	124	152	191	254
12.5	7/16	61	75	97	118	149	187
9	5/16	44	53	69	84	106	141

DETAILS OF SHOT SIZES
(nominal)

Desig.	Diameter		Pellets	
	mm	in	per 10 g	per oz
LG	9.1	.36	2	6
SG	8.4	.33	3	8
Spec.SG	7.6	.30	4	11
SSG	6.8	.27	5.1/2	15
AAA	5.2	.20	12.1/2	35
BB	4.1	.16	25	70
1	3.6	.14	36	100
3	3.3	.13	50	140
4	3.1	.12	60	170
5	2.8	.11	78	220
6	2.6	.10	95	270
7	2.4	.095	120	340
7.1/2	2.3	.09	140	400
8	2.2	.085	160	450
9	2.0	.08	210	580

g = grams

TABLE: SHOT SIZES

Courtesy: Eley

15.3 Punt gun and ram rod.

15.4 Demonstration of punt gunning.

16
Ferreting

Recommended reading:

Ferrets and Ferreting by W. Carnegie

(Nimrod Press)

16.1 Ferrets must be handled firmly yet carefully.

Ferrets

Ferreting is an ancient sport that is enjoyed by many sportsmen.

Ferrets are a domesticated strain of the wild polecat which is still to be found in some parts of the British Isles. Indeed, the dark brown ferrets with cream undercoats are known as polecats and are very similar to the wild ones. White or cream ferrets with pink eyes are also common and various colourations result from crossing the two.

Ferrets are used predominantly for rabbiting, although a small pygmy strain are used on rats. When entered into the holes or buries, ferrets are expected to work all the underground passage ways and evict the occupants.

Care of ferrets

Care should be taken in the first instance to purchase healthy and well-handled stock. It is of utmost importance for the ferret to willingly return to hand and allow itself to be picked up when its work is done. One will quickly and easily adapt to life in the wild should it not be picked up and will become a menace to game stocks and domestic poultry.

The ferrets should be comfortably housed in dry, draught-proof and escape-proof quarters. Most often they are kept individually in hutches with a separate sleeping compartment. Fresh hay or straw should be provided for bedding and the hutch must be regularly cleaned out to prevent it from smelling.

Ferrets will live equally well in larger compounds as a commune, providing they have been introduced into this system at an early age. The females (jills) will successfully breed and raise their litters together, although a few of the kits may be lost to the males (hobs).

A female will remain in season for several months unless mated. This has always been a problem for ferret owners. The choice lay between having an

16.2 Rabbits were introduced to the British Isles by the Normans and are the main quarry of the ferreter.

16.3 If ferrets and terriers are to be worked together they must be on friendly terms.

unwanted litter of kits or an unhealthy jill. A solution to this problem is now available in two forms. For the owner of several ferrets it is suggested that a vasectomy operation be carried out on a hob, thus making him infertile, but still capable of satisfying the needs of the jill. Alternatively, an injection of a drug (as used for bitches) by a veterinary surgeon will prevent the jill from coming into season.

Ferrets breed during the spring. Accordingly, there are usually a plentiful supply of young ferrets available for sale at the end of the summer.

They should be fed fresh meat daily, the quantity being judged according to appetite, and any surplus removed promptly, especially during the summer months when it will soon become putrefied. Bread and milk will suffice only as a temporary measure. Water should be available.

From the time they begin to be active, the kits should be handled regularly so that they are completely tame and show no inclination to bite. As they usually work loose, it is vital that they are easily caught.

Ferreting Rabbits

Apart from the morality of it, working ferrets is impractical when young rabbits are about. Therefore, ferreting is usually confined to late autumn and the winter months. If ferrets are worked on young rabbits difficulties will arise as, very likely, kills will be made beneath ground and the ferret will be reluctant to return to the surface.

Ferrets are transported in either carrying boxes or bags. The boxes must be well ventilated and, although popular, are cumbersome and the ferrets confined inside can make a great deal of noise by scratching. Bags, which should have a solid base and a drawstring, are probably more convenient and should also have adequate ventilation.

Nets used to place over the rabbit holes can either be purchased, or are easily made at home. The best nets are made of natural fibres, either left a natural colour or dyed green for camouflage. Man-made fibres are best avoided as they easily tangle and debris such as leaves and twigs cling to the net. After use, all nets must be thoroughly dried before being rolled up or else they will soon rot.

Other necessary items of equipment are a spade, a billhook and a sharp pocket knife.

An electronic locator or bleeper collar to put on the ferret is a useful aid for locating the exact position of the ferret underground and, at times, can save a lot of digging. Another useful asset is a reliable dog that will mark only the holes that are occupied.

Permission must be granted from the landowner or keeper before ferreting takes place. A reconnaissance trip is advisable to locate occupied burrows and to clear excess vegetation where necessary. This can save a lot of time on the actual day set aside for ferreting.

Usually the jills are worked first and are loose. Before they are entered, great care must be taken to place and firmly peg a net over every hole. A detailed inspection must be made of the area so that no hole is left un-netted, however obscure it may seem. This work must be carried out quietly and as quickly as possible.

The hob is normally used only to locate a jill that has not returned to the surface. She may have killed and be 'laying up', in which case the hob will probably drive her off the kill. Either a bleeper or a line may be attached to the hob so that his precise position is known. The only course of action may be to dig the ferret out, which is not always easy if there are stones or tree roots in the way.

The bolted rabbit

Bolting rabbits that have become entangled in the net should be quickly despatched and the net replaced with a new one. Often it is easier to kill the rabbit in the net before disentangling it. Some experienced rabbiters kill the rabbit with a blow on the back of the head, using the side of their hand. Generally the best and easiest method is to grip the rabbit across the loins with one hand, while the other hand is used to hold the rabbit's head immediately in front of the ears, forcing the head upwards whilst pulling downwards.

Preparation

As soon as the rabbit has been killed, it should be removed from the net and urine should be emptied from the bladder by pressure between the hind legs. Paunching should be carried out as quickly as possible, leaving the kidneys in place. However, some dealers prefer the rabbit not paunched, if it is intended to freeze them.

The legs should be 'hocked' so that the rabbit can be easily hung up. This is done by making a slit between the tendon and the bone on one hind leg just above the hock. The other hind leg should be pushed through the slit and the tendon cut near to the hock to prevent it slipping back out.

Sometimes ferrets are worked without nets. Bolted rabbits are either shot by waiting guns or are coursed by lurchers.

The responsibility of the ferret owner

An errant ferret should never be left to go wild. They are lethal killers and every effort must be made to capture it. As a last resort, if a ferret has failed to re-appear and it has not been located by digging, a live catch trap baited with fresh meat should be left in the vicinity of the burrows worked. It is recommended that all the holes are blocked, except either the one in which the ferret was originally entered or the main hole. The cage trap should be left in position near to the hole left open and inspected regularly. Alternatively, the carrying box may be left nearby in the hope that the ferret will settle down to sleep inside.

16.4 Electronic Ferret Finder

16.5 Rabbits will sometimes be holed up in some very awkward places.

17

Dogs

Flat Coat   **Curly Coat**

Chesapeake Bay

17.1 Retrievers

Breeds of working gun dogs

Retrievers

Golden
Labrador
Flat Coated
Curly Coated
Chesapeake Bay

Spaniels

English Springer
Welsh Springer
Cocker
Clumber
Field
Sussex
Irish Water
Brittany

H.P.R. (Hunter, pointer, retriever)

Vizsla
Weimaraner
German Short Haired Pointer
German Wire Haired Pointer
Munsterlander

Pointers and Setters

Pointer (English)
English Setter
Gordon Setter
Irish Setter
A dog licence is required for working gun dogs.

Gundogs and Terriers
Working value

A dog is a necessary item of equipment for any keeper but, in many cases, the relationship is much deeper than the dog being used merely as a tool. Many times it is the keeper's only companion during the day when he is at work and at night when on poacher patrol. An honest, hard working dog soon earns respect not only from its owner, but also from others involved.

The main value of a dog, as far as a keeper is concerned, is its nose; the ability it possesses to follow or identify a scent with the ease by which the human eye detects an object. Added to this invisible power are speed and intelligence. All this energy, however, needs to be channelled in a useful direction and many of a dog's natural instincts need to be curbed. Patience and understanding are required to train a dog. Patience to ensure that one lesson at a time is thoroughly learned before another is attempted, and understanding to reason as a dog does and to realise the necessity for basic obedience.

No gundog should be allowed to disrupt a shoot day. Genuine misdenmeanours do occur, but if there is any likelihood of it happening, then the dog should be left at home. A gun dog that continually whines or barks, or is allowed to chase round after birds during a drive, can be distracting and spoil the enjoyment of the rest of the team of guns.

Likewise, a beater's dog that reaches the heading of a drive before the beaters have hardly started, or one that runs out of the drive to retrieve birds it has seen shot, will also mar the pleasure of a day's shooting. Despite the wealth of advice and knowledge available, a well trained dog is often noticed and remarked upon, being an uncommon sight.

When criticism is levelled at a keeper's dog it must be remembered the many tasks it is expected to perform. Not only will it be worked on formal shoot days when control and steadiness are necessary, but it will also be used for rabbiting and driving in amongst other jobs. This work is the quickest way

Clumber

Field

Sussex

Brittany

17.2 Spaniels

of encouraging a dog to forget all that it has been taught in its early days. If possible, it is wisest to save the oldest dog for these purposes so that a young dog is not ruined early in its career. Also, with age, a dog will very likely learn to differentiate what is required of it for the individual tasks.

Often a "wild dog" is the best game finder, but its uses are somewhat limited if it is not under control and may not be trusted. It is understandably difficult to train a dog to range within fifteen yards (about 15 metres) when used for beating and then, perhaps, send it for two hundred yards (approximately 200 metres) after a runner. Given the right temperament, this can be done, but requires a great deal of time, patience and trust.

Choice of Breed

The choice of breed of gundog is up to the individual. Such varying temperaments can be found within individual breeds that it is impossible to lay down strict guidelines. Every dog possesses its own character and they are as diverse as those found in humans. No two are ever exactly alike.

The list given previously is divided into four categories and the choice of breed should be governed in some respect to the purpose the dog will be used for. The common choice is a labrador retriever which is generally considered to be a breed suited to driven shooting and picking up. They are, however, useful dogs for beating or rough shooting and, although they do not work with the style of a spaniel, they can be just as efficient. The Flat Coated Retriever, which was once very popular with keepers, has gone somewhat out of fashion and is generally considered to be more difficult to handle.

The Springer Spaniel is the second most popular choice. They are energetic and keen, and a very useful all-round dog, being good hunters and usually good retrievers. The disadvantage with Springers is that they require strict handling, without which they become headstrong and uncontrollable.

H.P.R. (Hunting, Pointing and Retrieving) breeds such as the German Short Haired Pointer and the Weimaraner are imports from the Continent that are gaining in popularity.

The fourth category are the pointers and setters. These are breeds that are used solely to locate the position of game. They are expected to range at a distance across open ground and when they identify the presence of game, they adopt a stance known as a "point". These breeds are not expected to retrieve, so their use is limited to working in conjunction with a retriever on open grouse or partridge grounds.

It is important to select strains that have been used for work, but first crosses between the retriever or spaniel breeds can make useful workers.

Vizsla

Weimaraner

17.3 Hunter, Pointer, and Retriever

Selection

Most young dogs are purchased at seven or eight weeks old. Dogs offered for sale at a later age should be viewed with caution. Sometimes these have developed some fault that may, or may not, affect their working potential. Genuine dogs are available, though, and purchasing one at a later stage has the advantage that a better judgment can be made of looks and temperament than is possible in an eight week old pup.

Even more caution should be exercised when a dog is offered free of charge if it is more than five or six months old. Often puppies have got completely out of control by this age and it is difficult, if not impossible, to instil subsequent discipline.

When a puppy is purchased it should be checked for obvious signs of ill health or weakness. The pedigree should be studied, if there is one, and it should be ascertained that both parents are from working lines. A large percentage of show blood should be avoided at all costs. Too much field trial breeding can also be a disadvantage as some lines may prove too excitable and hot (over keen) to be easily handled by the average keeper. If in doubt, advice should be sought from someone who is knowledgeable about working gun dogs. Should a wrong choice be made, it can be a costly mistake.

It is extremely difficult to select a dog with working potential from any litter of young pups. If one will carry a small object, it is a good sign. Some owners prefer a dog with a bold character, while others choose a more gentle and timid nature. These characteristics may be quite obvious when a litter is viewed, but frequently puppies alter as they grow older and depending upon what conditions they are kept under.

It is impossible to judge what an eight-week old puppy will be like when it has matured, so it really is a question of paying the money and taking your choice.

The "look" in a puppy's eye is the best guideline at a later age. A kind, honest eye will give an indication to the nature of the animal. One should not be bought that averts its gaze or has a wicked glint. The will to please its master is the most valued quality in any working dog.

Which sex is another difficult decision. The old saying that a bitch is a nuisance six weeks of the year and a dog is a nuisance all year is sometimes quite true. Most keepers' dogs are kept in kennels, so these problems are lessened. Obviously a bitch should not be worked with dogs when she is in season. An injection is available that will delay or suppress the onset of heat so a discussion with a veterinary surgeon may safely overcome this problem.

17.4 A Fell type Terrier. *Northern gamekeepers often prefer a terrier that is able to kill a fox underground.*

17.5 Will they be good workers? Puppies should be bred from parents with working backgrounds, but not necessarily field trial.

A dog confined in a kennel will be unable to wander, but may sometimes be more interested in bitches than work when out shooting. The most undesirable habit a dog has is cocking his leg whenever and wherever he chooses.

Care

Caring for the working dog is mainly a matter of common sense. It should be housed in a draught-proof and escape-proof kennel and run. A kennel four feet (1 metre) square and a run eight feet (2.5 metres) by four feet (1 metre) will adequately house one or two labradors. It is easier to keep clean if the run is concreted or paved, and has some form of drainage. Bedding is a matter of choice. Wheat straw is preferable. There is no need to provide bedding at all in the summer months and, if used in winter, it should never be allowed to get wet. Raised wooden benches are draught free and will keep drier. A dog should not be expected to lay directly on concrete. Weld mesh panels are ideal for constructing the run. Puppies chew and the less exposed wood there is inside the kennel, the less damage will be done.

At first, the puppy should be fed three or four times a day and its diet should be well balanced and contain some milk. It is advisable to obtain a food supply for a few days when buying a puppy so that its diet can be changed slowly. Opinions differ greatly on methods of feeding, but a good quality "all in one" feed, either pellets or coarse meal, should supply a balanced diet with no mess and very little preparation.

As the puppy grows, the number of feeds should be reduced until at maturity only one a day is given. Exceptions should be made for pregnant bitches and hard-working dogs, when the amount should be increased and divided between two meals.

Fresh, clean water must be available at all times.

Immunity to disease passed on to her puppies from the dam will decrease and vaccination should be carried out by three months of age. Apart from the usual distemper and hepatitis vaccines, protection should be provided against the highly infectious parvo virus. It is advisable also to vaccinate against leptospirosis, a disease which is fatal and is contracted from rats. All working dogs are likely to come into contact with rats and vaccination is particularly important for terriers.

Worming should be carried out periodically and skin vermin such as fleas and lice should be dealt with when necessary.

Any sign of discomfort in the ears should be attended to and a vet consulted if the condition persists. Harmful complications may set in which could lead to eventual deafness if the infection is left untreated.

17.6 A kind, honest eye is an *indication of the nature of a dog. The will to please is the most valued quality.*

17.7 Puppies should not require supplementary feeding until at least three weeks of age.

Formal training

Formal training does not usually begin until at least six months of age. Before then, some basic discipline should be instilled and bad habits such as chasing and noisiness should be discouraged. The puppy should also be accustomed to distant gun fire, car travel, traffic, livestock, poultry, etc., whenever the opportunity permits.

Intensive formal training commences with teaching basic obedience. This should never be neglected as it is the mainstay of a working dog's usefulness. It does not matter how clever or gifted a dog is; if the basic discipline is lacking, its qualities are wasted.

Training should be done with kindness but firmness and involves channelling a dog's natural instincts in a direction that is beneficial to the shooting man. If a dog is of a sensitive nature, the tone of voice is often as much chastisement as is necessary. A bolder dog may need harsher treatment and a tap with a thin, swishy stick at the crucial moment may prove most effective. A dog should never be beaten into submission. If punishment is necessary, then a violent shaking by the scruff of the neck is the best method.

Lessons are best taught away from the kennels and a puppy should be housed on its own during training. One kept indoors is best kennelled during this period as this focusses its attention entirely on training sessions. The sessions should be no longer than thirty minutes at the most, and must not be allowed to become boring. Any feeling of dissent between pupil and teacher should be realised and the dog returned to the kennel before any irreparable harm is caused by impatience. Praise should be given whenever the correct action has been taken. If the pupil voluntarily returns to heel when running free, a fuss should be made of it so that an association forms between returning to the handler and being petted. A young dog should be persuaded that it is a pleasure to be by its master's side.

At all times a handler must attempt to think as the dog thinks. The most common fault in training is to administer some form of chastisement for disobedience when the dog has returned to heel. It must be realised that a puppy's mind is relatively simple and it judges the handler's reaction to its last deed. In the example previously stated, the dog thinks it is being punished for its last action, which was returning to heel. Any crimes committed must be punished where and when they happen. Equally, discipline must be maintained at the same standard continually. It is a waste of time to correct a fault one day and allow it to go uncorrected another. The same level of obedience must be maintained at all times.

17.8 A puppy should be experienced on dummies before being introduced to game.

17.9 There must be adequate numbers of dogs to pick up game. Three teams of dogs awaiting their owners on the grouse moor.

By six months of age an assessment can be made of the puppy's temperament, and this must be taken into consideration when training begins and allowances made accordingly.

Opinions differ as to the order in which the basic disciplines are taught. But the most important command a puppy needs to learn is "NO". The other fundamental commands are "Heel", "come here", "sit", "stay", and "fetch" (or "hi-lost" which is the common command for seeking and bringing back). Orders should be given vocally and also by signals with a whistle and the hands.

Lesson 1

The first lesson is to accustom the puppy to walking on a lead. It should be positioned with its head close to the handler's left knee. A "choker" lead should be used and at first a few sharp jerks will be required to keep the puppy in the correct position. Making use of a narrow pathway will help achieve this. The word "heel" should be repeated, punctuated with praise when the pupil is doing the right thing. Once it is judged that the puppy will stay in position, then the lead can be allowed to drag on the ground and eventually be removed. At the slightest sign of misbehaviour, the command "no" must be given harshly and obedience enforced.

A sensitive puppy will often sit down and refuse to move if it is unsure of itself. This may happen at any stage during training and a kind tone of voice and encouragement will be needed to persuade it to do what is required and gain confidence.

A thin, swishy stick can be used to prevent a bolder dog from trying to push past the handler's knee. Waived in front of the animal's head, it can be quite effective. A bold dog will often take little notice of a verbal reprimand and may require more severe punishment by way of a shaking.

Some trainers allow dogs to make mistakes which they then correct, and others believe it better to prevent mistakes happening. Whichever method is chosen, it should be remembered that, with most dogs, it is easier to slacken off control than it is to regain it once lost.

Lesson 2

When a puppy can be trusted to walk to heel off the lead, then the next command should be taught. A lead should be used at first to control the pupil which should be walked along at heel. When the handler stops, the command "sit" is given and practiced until the pupil automatically sits as soon as the handler stops when it is off the lead. A sensitive puppy will often lay down or

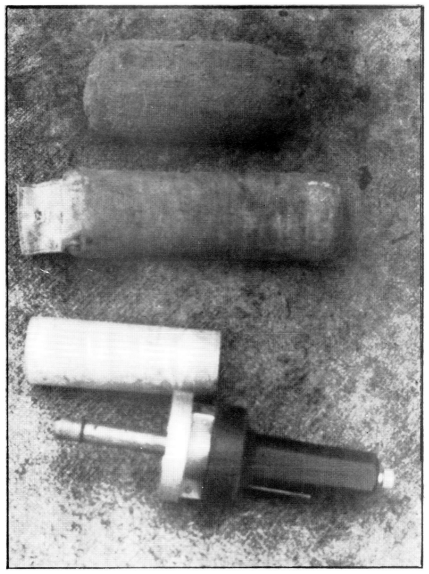

17.11 Dummies for dog training can be made from a piece of wood covered with an old sock (above) or canvas. Rabbit skin or game birds' wings can be fixed to make the dummy more realistic. Plastic dummies can be launched from the dummy launcher illustrated bottom. This is fired by a blank .22 bullet which also produces the sound of gunshot.

even roll over on its back, but unless obedience trial work is intended, then this should be considered as obeying the word "sit".

Lesson 3

The next step is to teach the pupil to stay. Once again, at first on the lead, the puppy should be told to "sit". The handler should then back away from the pupil, alternating the command "sit" with "stay". Whenever the puppy attempts to move, it should be firmly placed back in the sitting position on the exact spot it moved from. A first a distance of a couple of yards is sufficient and at this stage the handler should always return to the pupil and give lavish praise. A final test of obedience to "stay" is for the handler to walk in a wide circle around the pupil; if no attempt is made by the puppy to move when it changes its head direction when following the handler's movements, it can be assumed that the lesson is learnt. It must also be trusted to stay in position when the handler is out of sight.

Lesson 4

After this lesson, the pupil can be taught to "come here". Whenever it is called to the handler and returns quickly, it should be praised. At all times this is best done by the tone of voice and by stroking under the chin. This will encourage the puppy to hold its head up, a useful prelude for the next lesson of retrieving. Rewards of food are not recommended for gun dogs, as this encourages them to drop the dummy instead of delivering it to hand when retrieving.

All these commands can be practiced at odd times during free running exercise. If a puppy is recalled to the handler, praised, and then allowed to run on again, it is more likely to return of its own free will than it is if only called in when there are instructions to be obeyed. It is useful to use a particular command when the puppy is allowed to run free and enjoy itself.

Lesson 5

The final basic command the pupil is taught is "Hi lost" or "fetch" or "seek" as some owners prefer.

So far as keepers" dogs are concerned, this is when steadiness should be concentrated on.

A small dummy should be used at first. The pupil should be sat at heel and gently restrained by either a lead or the hand while the dummy is thrown a few yards. A place should be chosen where the dummy will be clearly visible. The puppy should be quickly released and encouraged as it attempts to pick up the dummy. At first it will probably play with it, but once it has actually got hold of the dummy, it should immediately be called in to the handler and praised. If there is a reluctance to pick up the dummy, then it should be used to tease the puppy into grabbing hold of it; also, the puppy should be allowed to run in towards the dummy as soon as it is thrown. However, as soon as the pupil will pick it up readily, then these undesirable practices must be immediately stopped before bad habits are learned.

Three problems commonly arise during retrieving. Often the pupil is reluctant to return to the handler with the dummy. On no account must it be chased; the best course of action is for the handler to turn his back and run away or kneel down and call the pupil. When the puppy realises that no game is likely to ensue and that it may be left behind, it usually decides to bring the dummy to hand. If a puppy is reluctant to let go of the dummy, then light pressure on the toes or the lips against the teeth will solve this problem. The dummy should never be the subject of a tug of war, nor should pain be inflicted on the pupil in an attempt to procure release.

The third common problem is when the pupil drops the dummy before it reaches the handler. Once again, this can usually be overcome by running away from the puppy and even taking the dummy while still in motion.

Patience and understanding will normally overcome these problems, but occasionally a puppy will completely refuse to pick up a dummy. Other objects can be substituted, or even a bone. As a last resort, cold game can be tried, but this should never normally be used until a puppy is experienced and reliable on dummy work. Alternatively, the dummy can be attached to a length of string and jerked as the puppy approaches.

Retrieving work can be extended once the initial lesson has been learned. Steadiness should be concentrated on and emphasised by dummies being thrown and the puppy made to watch while the handler picks them up. The pupil must be made to realise that it will not be expected to retrieve everything that it has seen fall. Alternatively, dummies should be hidden out of view of the dog and the pupil made to use his nose to search for them. Various exercises can be combined to encourage steadiness and control, while developing the puppy's own initiative.

An excellent exercise at this stage to test the pupil's ability is the following-

The handler should walk with the puppy at heel off the lead. The command should be given to sit and stay while the handler walks a few yards further on. The dummy should then be thrown to land behind the pupil and the handler continues to walk away. When at a reasonable distance, the pupil should be recalled to heel and commanded to sit. It should then be sent back for the retrieve.

Advanced Training

Further lessons are extremely useful, but are often not considered necessary by keepers. The puppy can be taught to stop on command at a distance. At first this is done using a long whistle blast and commanding "stay" with the pupil at heel. Once understood, the exercise should be practiced with the puppy running free and then when being recalled. Finally, it should be possible to stop the dog on its way to a retrieve. Care must be taken not to over-do this lesson because it may discourage the pupil from using its own initiative.

Final requirements are teaching the puppy to accept directional hand signals from the handler at a distance. At first this is done by throwing dummies either side of the dog and encouraging it to pick first whichever the handler indicates by hand signal. This lesson can progress until the pupil can be directed in any given direction at will. Once again care must be taken not to produce a dog that reacts automatically and relies entirely on the handler to direct it on to a retrieve. This advanced handling, though, can be very useful when a dog is required to retrieve on the far side of a thick hedge or a river. "Style", that quality that is deemed so important by the field trial fraternity, is of little benefit to the keeper.

Hunting usually comes naturally to a working bred dog, but it needs to be controlled. A keeper's dog in the beating line will be required to work within a radius of approximately fifteen yards (15 metres). When it is used for picking up, it will be expected to cover a far greater distance and, for this reason, it is useful to use a separate command for either task. "Hi lost" can be used when there is game to pick up, and some other order when the dog is used to flush birds.

Introduction to dead game

Until a puppy has perfected dummy work, it should not be introduced to retrieving game. When the time comes that it is ready, then only fresh cold game should be used. Avoid badly damaged birds and pigeons whose feathers are loose and can be off-putting to a young dog. Fur and feather must both be introduced and encouragement may be necessary before the puppy will realise what is required. Partridges are an ideal size to start a puppy on. An elastic band to hold the wings in place may be advisable to begin with, or even covering with a sock, if there is reluctance to pick game up.

Warm game should not be used until cold game is readily and easily retrieved. It is advisable to avoid sending a puppy for a runner in its first season. Not only does it lack the experience to handle the bird, which may result in damage being caused, but it will also encourage the young dog to become unsteady. Occasionally, a young dog will damage game through inexperience.

Field trial enthusiasts go to great lengths to include every facet of training. For the average keeper a dog that is steady, obedient and can use its own common sense is all that is required. Much can be learnt by a young dog from accompanying its master on his daily feed and trapping rounds. A covey of released French partridges or rabbits hopping around are fine tests of steadiness. Every opportunity should be taken to establish obedience when temptation presents itself.

Introduction to the shooting field

The introduction to the shooting field is a traumatic experience for a young dog. Although it should be experienced in working cover and water, and although it will be reliable with regard to retrieving and steadiness, there is nothing that can be done previously to simulate the hustle and bustle of a shoot day. The noise of shooting, sticks tapping, whistles and numbers of people, will all create an atmosphere that the puppy will find overwhelming. In some the reaction is to get over excited and go to pieces while, in others, to withdraw and become timid. Patience will be required and, providing the groundwork has been thoroughly done at home, the young dog will soon settle down and remember its lessons.

A puppy should be familiar with distant gun fire from an early age and later training should have included this. Even so, some sensitive dogs show dislike of a gun being fired frequently close by when they are expected to stand next to the gun. The ideal introduction to a shoot day for a puppy used for picking up or by a standing gun is for the handler to spare the time to stand well back from the shooting. Normally, when the young dog is able to see what is happening and probably given one or two easy retrieves (no more), its confidence will be established.

Many young dogs are slightly nervous, which is totally different to being gun shy, when the animal is absolutely terrified.

Some trainers do not advocate introducing a young dog to the shooting field until it is at least a year old. Others believe that, providing the puppy has proved trustworthy in its basic training, then it will benefit from the experience at an earlier age. Whatever the decision, all young dogs should be brought on gradually. Harm will be done if the young dog is allowed or expected to hunt freely and be over faced with retrieving. The first season should be viewed as an extension of training and every effort should be made in maintaining obedience and encouraging good behaviour to be a natural reaction. One of the first lessons the pupil should learn is that it is not required to work all the time, so sessions of walking to heel will be of utmost value, as will watching other dogs work. It will be necessary to concentrate primarily on the puppy.

A young dog that is uncontrollable in the shooting field will **NOT** improve with age and will cause disruption and become unpopular with all concerned. A puppy that has been quick to learn its lessons will just as quickly learn bad habits from other dogs or due to lack of concentration of the handler. To correct these bad habits is exceedingly difficult, if not impossible, once they have been allowed to become established.

As previously mentioned, most keepers need a dog's services for other chores besides beating or picking up. At the end of the winter, rabbiting is usually part of seasonal duties and later in the summer, "driving" or "dogging in" will be necessary. If possible, it is wisest to use the older and more experienced dogs for these chores and confine the youngster to one or two seasons of beating to begin with. This imprints steadiness in the mind, prior to getting involved in wilder pursuits.

Ideally, all dogs should be soft mouthed and retrieve live game tenderly to hand. In some cases dogs tend to become rougher with birds as they get older, especially if they have been used a lot for driving in or beating. They then realise that if they react quickly enough, it is possible for them to "peg" a live bird.

A dog that is regularly hard mouthed and flattens live birds should not be kept and, if a pet home cannot be found, it should be destroyed. On no account should it be bred from because hard mouth is considered to be a hereditary factor.

Breeding

A dog that shows signs of blindness or hip displasia (confirmed by an X-ray) or any other congenital fault, must not be bred from either, as these too are hereditary and are already far too common in some of the working gun-dog breeds.

No bitch should be bred from without due consideration. The venture may be costly if veterinary attention is needed and if puppies cannot be sold.

The choice of sire should be a sound, sensible working dog. The bitch will be on heat for approximately three weeks, during which the most likely time she will accept the dog is on or around the twelfth day. Even when mated by one dog, she will still accept others, so care must be taken throughout the heat period. If unwanted mating occurs, an injection within twenty-four hours by a veterinary surgeon will eliminate the risk of pregnancy.

The gestation period is about sixty three days, during which time the bitch should be well fed. In the later stages, extra food should be given, preferably divided into two meals daily, but the bitch should not be permitted to become too fat.

She should be allowed to whelp in familiar surroundings without undue disturbance. A warm bed of straw or newspaper should be provided and, if the weather is very cold, heat should be supplied by an infra red lamp hung well out of reach. Many bitches, housed outdoors permanently, dislike too much extra heat and will move their puppies away from the area if possible.

If, during whelping, there is obvious distress or a delay of more than two hours between the arrival of puppies, then veterinary advice should be sought.

Rearing

The bitch should provide the puppies with sufficient milk for at least three weeks. However, if a litter is extra large or the bitch cannot feed them properly for some reason, supplementary feeding will be necessary. It is not generally practical to rear more than eight, so any in excess should be culled at birth. When doing this, it should be remembered that in present times, bitches are much easier to sell than dogs.

Docking, or the removal of dew claws, should be carried out within a few days of birth.

Solid food can be gradually introduced at three to four weeks, at first well moistened. Amounts should be gradually increased until the puppies are fully weaned by six or seven weeks and kept away from their dam.

The bitch should not be worked for the last few weeks of pregnancy, nor until her milk has dried up and the skin retracted. To work her before this is risking her getting badly torn on barbed wire.

General care

It is unfair to expect a dog to work if it is unfit, and it will not get fit confined in a kennel. Many keepers' dogs get fit by being used for driving in, but if this is not the case then extra exercise must be given prior to the shooting season.

Attention should be paid to the coats of long-haired breeds, particularly spaniels whose coats easily become matted. It does no harm to trim some of the hair, particularly around the ears and between the toes. Burrs or cleavers or brambles soon become entangled in the fur if not removed or prevented from doing so by trimming.

After work the dog should be inspected for cuts or thorns, etc; in the feet and eyes particularly. Serious injuries should be dealt with by a veterinary surgeon. A common site for cuts is the skin where the front of the thigh joins the body.

Ears should also be inspected occasionally, especially if the dog has been involved in working in water. Any discomfort shown by scratching or head shaking should be noted and the vet consulted. Vaccinations should be kept up to date and boosters given when necessary. Dogs from all over the country will be brought into contact with each other in the shooting season, thus increasing the risk of infection.

Picking up

A novice picker-up can learn much from watching other experienced dogs and handlers. No attempt should be made to rush a puppy into action. If all of the first season and part of the second are spent in allowing the young dog to acquire experience, while still retaining discipline, it is time well spent. A good, honest working dog is a pleasure to handle and will remain so for the subsequent ten years if properly trained to begin with.

An experienced dog that can be trusted should be allowed to get on with its work without undue interference. More often than not its nose will tell it better than the eyes of its handler where a bird has gone.

Previous thought should be given before directions are given. Allowance for scenting conditions and wind direction must be considered. The dog should not be recalled unless the handler is absolutely certain that it is working in the wrong direction.

Wounded game does not always do what is expected of it and will often be above the ground in a bush or below ground in a rabbit hole. If the dog is reliable, it should be trusted. An experienced dog will often hear whether a bird is hit.

Birds are often marked down "dead" by a gun when the wing has been broken close to the body. When this happens the "dead" bird will have immediately run and finding it may take some time. Wounded game is quite capable of swimming and will sometimes deliberately take to water. Ducks will dive.

To avoid fouling the "line" it is wise to send only one dog at first on an unseen runner.

Wounded birds should be killed as soon as possible when retrieved. The best method is by hitting on the head with a stick or similar object.

The best picker-up is one who goes unnoticed. His task should be to pick up dead and wounded birds that have fallen away from the guns. There is no value in picking up dead birds laying in the open that can be easily gathered by hand, although a search of the area should be made later. For humane reasons, it is far better to pick half as many wounded birds that would have otherwise met with a lingering death.

Before the beginning of every shoot day, the picker-up should ascertain where he is allowed to go. Some drives may be planned for later in the day where birds have fallen from an earlier drive. On no account should a picker up allow his dogs to disturb these areas. If there is any risk of a dog running in, then it should be kept on a lead.

Noisy handling by voice or whistle should also be kept to a minimum as game already made nervous by gunfire will become increasingly disturbed by other noise.

Enquiries should also be made as to whether picking up can be conducted during a drive or whether it should be left until after the signal is given for the end of the drive. Guns and keepers frequently dislike dogs working in view while a drive is in progress. Exceptions are often made, though, if a picker up is positioned in cover well out of sight when birds, particularly strong runners, may be lost if there is a delay in sending a dog.

Great care must be taken when picking up near public roads or railways. A dog hot on the heels of a runner is unlikely to take any heed of the handler or be aware of the danger from passing traffic. Another hazard likely to occur is when crop spraying is taking place. Some of these sprays are lethal, as are slug pellets (**Metaldehyde**) A dog should not, therefore, be allowed to drink contaminated water or to otherwise have direct contact with these chemicals.

Electric fencing, particularly sheep fencing, can be very disconcerting if a dog should make contact with it and receive a shock. It is particularly unnerving for inexperienced young dogs and they may take several hours to regain confidence after such an unpleasant incident.

A dog working in dry and dusty conditions will require plenty of fresh drinking water and a supply should be made available whenever possible if there are no natural sources.

At the end of the day, the dog should be dried off if necessary, fed and provided with a dry bed of straw.

Summary

It is very nearly impossible to find a dog that is perfect in every way. Many faults are caused by bad training or handling, and others by physical defects. Some of these are considered to be hereditary, such as hard mouth, whining, over or under-shot jaws. Also, ailments such as lameness caused by hip displasia and blindness by progressive retinal atrophy or cataracts. Dogs suffering with any of these afflictions must not be bred from. Other faults can either be caused by lack of ability of the dog, poor nose or lack of drive, etc.., or the failure of the handler to maintain control such as running in, not walking to heel or taking birds from other dogs, a crime that will induce hard mouth in others. Time is well spent in basic training and developing a mutual trust. The cost of owning a bad dog is the same as owning a good one. The presence of a badly trained or handled dog on a shoot day is unpleasant for guns or pickers up and an embarrassment to its owner. The pleasure derived from the company of a reliable and trustworthy friend is immeasurable. But it is only obtained by patience, understanding and paying attention to the dog at all times.

Terriers

Terriers have characters all of their own and although it is impossible to train them as a gun dog is trained, some discipline must be instilled.

A terrier has two natural instincts, firstly to please itself, and secondly to kill. A terrier is of the opinion that it is bigger and better than anything else, no matter what its breeding, and prefers to act independently.

A good terrier is a very useful tool to any keeper, particularly for dealing with all kinds of vermin. The more amenable ones are useful for beating and rabbiting, but an effort should be made to persuade them not to touch feathered species.

A young terrier should not be entered to a fox until it is at least a year old. It should be encouraged to bark and evict the fox rather than to attempt to kill it, although many northern keepers prefer a terrier that is strong and brave enough to kill. It is a great asset to have the sort of dog that will come out when called. Terriers seem oblivious to pain when working and sometimes get blocked in underground, in which case they have to be dug out.

Some large earths are a complex structure of tunnels and chambers and a bleeper similar to those used for ferrets is an invaluable aid to locating the terrier's position within.

On no account should a terrier be entered to a badger. This is illegal and the strong jaws of a badger can render severe damage to the dog.

Any injuries suffered should be carefully washed and cleaned with antiseptic and veterinary attention sought if required. Bites easily turn septic and an antibiotic injection may be advisable. If a terrier is used for ratting it should be vaccinated against leptospirosis, a highly infectious disease carried by rats.

Dirt should also be removed from the eyes and mouth when necessary.

The breed of a terrier is not important, providing it is from working stock and of the right size.

Ideally it should be possible to span the dog around the chest with the hands, and the fingers should meet.

The docked tail should have been left long enough for it to be grabbed hold of. Often this is the only part of a terrier that is visible and the only method of withdrawing it from a hole. At other times it is advisable to pick the dog up by the scruff of the neck. In a heated moment it may accidentally bite its owner if grabbed hold of anywhere else.

Whether it is smooth, broken or rough coated is purely a matter of personal choice. Much cross breeding has been done to produce the perfect working terrier, but opinions differ over this. Some keepers prefer a short-legged terrier, others a longer-legged type, but what is of importance is that it is small enough to do the work required.

At present times, two categories predominate - the Jack Russel type and the Fell Terrier. The latter is a general term which usually encompasses a type of terrier of any colour, but with very little white, often being fairly long-legged and having a broken or rough coat.

Most working terriers carry a predominance of either Jack Russel, Lakeland or Border Terrier in their ancestry.

Guard Dogs

The training of dogs for protection work is a specialised subject. No chances should be taken in producing the lethal weapon that a German Shepherd (or other breed) becomes when trained for security work. Most keepers who find they have the need for such an animal acquire rejects from the Police Dog Training Centres or from experienced trainers.

17.12 A field trial provides simulated shooting conditions during which dogs are judged for their working ability and style.

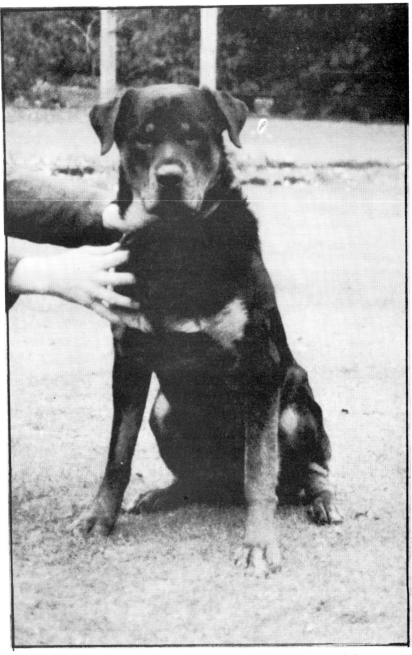

17.13 The Rottweiler is now one of the most popular guard dogs.

18
LEGAL ASPECTS
of
FIELD SPORTS

My sincere and very grateful thanks for their assistance in helping to unravel the complexities of the law go to Mr. D. Taylor and Mr. M.J.W. Churchouse, Secretary, East Anglian Game Protection Society, Norwich NR1 4DX.

'THE VILLAGE POACHER'

Legal Aspects

The Law as stated in this chapter applies only to England and Wales and, to the best of my knowledge, is correct. Scotland very often has its own statutes, which will differ from English Law. However, the close seasons for game and deer have been included.

Legal definitions to some of the words used appear at the end of the chapter and careful reference should be made to these.

General Position

The law is a very complex subject and some of the game laws have been in force since the first half of the last century.

A general guidance has been given of many of the laws that may be used for or against a gamekeeper in the nature of his work. Changes are continually being made and qualified guidance must be sought should it be needed. Copies of relevant Acts of Parliament are obtainable from Her Majesty's Stationery Offices.

In recent years legislation in the *Wildlife and Countryside Act* of 1981 has affected many aspects of a gamekeeper's duties. Game and Poaching Laws have been introduced over the years to protect sporting interests and game.

As a general rule, wild animals are not classed as the property of anyone and cannot, therefore, be stolen. However, domestic animals and livestock are classified as property and can therefore be stolen as can wild animals that have been tamed or are ordinarily kept in captivity. Carcases of wild animals can also be deemed the property of a person.

Any incidents of law breaking that do occur should be reported to the police at the earliest possible time. This can often prove difficult, though, due to the nature of the crime and the place where it may have taken place.

Any articles that have been left behind, e.g., guns, dead game, etc. should be kept as they may be used in evidence at a later date. The dead game (or fish) should be carefully labelled with full details (date, location, etc.) and placed in a deep freezer if possible.

Accurate and detailed notes should be made immediately of the time, location, description and conversation or any other event that took place. Due to the time lapse between the incident and the offender being brought to court, these detailed notes will prove invaluable. They are only acceptable, though, if they have been obviously made at the time and have not been altered at any time afterwards. It does not matter if the notes have been made on a scrap of paper such as a cigarette packet as long as they are in their original form.

There are many points of contention that involve gamekeepers. Two, in particular, are mentioned below as opinions and facts often vary.

1. Looking for game wounded on one person's land that has crossed on to some other person's land.

If it has fallen dead it can be collected. Although in practice it is not permitted to search for wounded game, should a search be made, a gun should never be carried as the offence of trespass in pursuit of game is technically committed. In every case it is wise to obtain permission first.

2. The shooting of dogs and cats.

Cats are only protected by the *Cruelty to Animals Act.*

The legal situation concerning the shooting of dogs is as follows: To kill, shoot or injure another person's dog, without legal justification, is a wrong, actionable at common law. Legal justification arises from the statutory provisions relating to the protection of livestock from dogs. In civil proceedings for the killing or injuring of a dog, it is a defence to prove (the onus of proof being on the defendant) that he acted for the protection of any livestock and was a person entitled so to act - *Animals Act,* 1971 Section 9(1) (a) and that within 48 hours of the killing or injury the defendant gave notice to an officer in charge of a Police Station. A person is entitled to act for the protection of his livestock if, and only if:

a. The livestock belongs to him or to any person under whose express or implied authority he is acting, and

b. The livestock was not killed or injured on land on to which it had strayed and either the dog belonged to the occupier of that land or its presence there was authorised by him.

Please note that the term "livestock" only includes deer not in a wild state and pheasants, partridges and grouse while in captivity. *Animals Act,* 1971 Section II.

A good relationship with the local police force is beneficial when various cases of law breaking occur. Successful prosecutions are probably one of the best deterrents and are only obtained with the prompt co-operation and genuine interest of the police. As the law is very complicated concerning game, several laws may be broken by one action of the offender. In many cases this involves different parties, e.g. the land owner, the police, etc., bringing separate prosecutions, an expensive and time-consuming process. The East Anglian Game Protection Society has eliminated many of these problems. This Society was established at the end of the last century and charges an annual membership fee to each of its members. When a poaching offence takes place on a member's land, the Society undertakes the prosecution for a nominal charge, the rest of the costs coming from the Society's funds. Being experts in this area of the law, the case is presented skilfully, eliminating the possibility of having up to four separate prosecutors, and having the full co-operation of the police.

One last point that frequently causes dispute between a gamekeeper and the public is the use of footpaths and bridleways. These are defined on page 335. The extent of the right of the public to use these highways is not very clearly defined. Their use is for the purpose of legitimate travel and is subject to a reasonable and proper use of such. A person who uses the highway for other purposes and not with a legitimate object must be presumed to have gone there for those purposes and as against the owner of the soil of the highway, he may be treated as a trespasser.

WILDLIFE AND COUNTRYSIDE ACT 1981

BIRDS

The following schedules cover any bird which is a resident or visitor to Great Britain existing in a wild state. Game birds are not included as they are covered by the Game Acts.

SCHEDULE 1 PART 1

SPECIAL PROTECTION - involving heavy fines for the destruction of birds including the species listed opposite.: This protection extends to the taking or destruction of nests, eggs and young.

BIRDS OF PREY
  BARN OWL
  SNOWY OWL
  HONEY BUZZARD
  GOLDEN EAGLE
  WHITE TAILED EAGLE
  GYR FALCON
  GOSHAWK
  HARRIERS (All Species)
  HOBBY
  RED KITE
  MERLIN
  OSPREY
  PEREGRINE
  RED BACKED SHRIKE

OTHERS
  STONE CURLEW
  KINGFISHER
  COMMON QUAIL
  BEWICKS SWAN
  WHOOPER SWAN
  LONG TAILED DUCK
  GARGANEY
  SCAUP
  COMMON SCOTER
  VELVET SCOTER
  DIVERS (All Species)

ORDINARY PROTECTION - incurring lesser fines is offered to all other species of birds including those listed below, but excluding those listed in Schedule 2

KESTREL

SPARROWHAWK

BUZZARD

ALL OTHER OWL SPECIES

HERON

MERGANSER

CORMORANT

MUTE SWAN

JACK SNIPE

GREAT SNIPE

Schedule 1 Part 2

Birds specially protected during the close season, but which may be killed or taken outside this period (1 February-31 August or 21 February-31 August below high water mark).

GOLDENEYE

PINTAIL

GREYLAG GOOSE (in Outer Hebrides, Caithness, Sutherland and Wester Ross only).

Schedule 2 Part 1

Birds which are protected during the close season (as above) but which may be killed or taken outside this period.

COOT   TUFTED DUCK

GADWALL

GOLDENEYE

CANADA GOOSE

GREYLAG GOOSE

PINKFOOTED GOOSE

WHITE FRONTED GOOSE (in England and Wales only)

MALLARD

MOORHEN

PINTAIL

GOLDEN PLOVER

POCHARD

SHOVELER

TEAL

WIGEON

CAPERCAILLIE (close season 1 February-30 September)

COMMON SNIPE (close season 1 February-11 August)

WOODCOCK (close season 1 February-30 September, in Scotland 1 February-31 August)

All species with the exception of Capercaillie included in Schedule 2 Part 1 are covered by an order made by the Secretary of State for the Environment to suspend shooting during periods of hard weather. This ban is announced via radio, T.V. and the press.

Schedule 2 Part 2

Birds which may be killed or taken by authorised persons at all times by approved methods (see pages 313/4).

GREAT BLACK-BACKED GULL

LESSER BLACK-BACKED GULL

HERRING GULL

JACKDAW

JAY

MAGPIE

FERAL PIGEON

WOOD PIGEON

ROOK

HOUSE SPARROW

STARLING

CARRION CROW

HOODED CROW

COLLARED DOVE

Schedule 3 Part 2

Birds which may be sold dead at all times.

FERAL PIGEON

WOOD PIGEON

Schedule 3 Part 3

Birds which may be sold dead from 1 Sept-28 Feb.

CAPERCAILLIE

COOT

TUFTED DUCK

MALLARD

PINTAIL

POCHARD

SHOVELER

TEAL

WIGEON

GOLDEN PLOVER

COMMON SNIPE

WOODCOCK

Shooting Seasons - Dates inclusive

Wild Duck, Geese and Waders

1 September - 31 January

1 September - 20 February (except waders) below the high water mark of ordinary spring tides.

WILDFOWL - GEESE

CANADA*

GREYLAG*

PINKFOOTED*

WHITEFRONTED* (in England and Wales only)

DUCKS

   COMMON POCHARD

   GADWALL*

   GOLDENEYE*

   MALLARD

   PINTAIL

   SHOVELER

   TUFTED

   TEAL

   WIGEON

WADERS

   GOLDEN PLOVER

   COOT

   MOORHEN*

* Species that may not be sold dead.

The following birds are subject to an S16 licence. The *Wildlife and Countryside Act,* 1981 makes provision for the killing of certain species in certain circumstances, e.g. when it is necessary for the prevention of serious damage to crops, vegetables, fruit, livestock, growing timber and fisheries, etc.

THROUGHOUT THE YEAR

   BARNACLE GOOSE

   BRENT GOOSE

   BULLFINCH

   CORMORANT

   GOOSANDER

   OYSTER CATCHER

   SHAG

DURING THE CLOSE SEASON
    CANADA GOOSE
    GREYLAG GOOSE
    PINKFOOTED GOOSE
    WHITEFRONTED GOOSE

NB. This exception applies to any wild bird other than the birds included in Schedule 1, *Wildlife and Countryside Act,* 1981.

Animals

Schedule 5

Animals that are fully protected include:
    OTTER
    BATS (All Species)
    RED SQUIRREL
    WILD CAT
    PINE MARTEN

Schedule 6

Animals which may not be killed or taken by certain methods include (see page 312):
    WILD CAT
    BADGER (see page 312)
    HEDGEHOG
    POLE CAT
    PINE MARTEN

Approved methods of control

Are restricted by various Acts of Parliament

Trapping (Pests Act 1954)

Approved Spring Traps

  FOR RABBITS

  FENN MARK I (Rabbit Trap)

  JUBY

  IMBRA MARK I and II

  FENN MARK VI (Vermin Trap)

FOR SMALL MAMMALIAN PREDATORS i.e. Stoats, weasels, rats and squirrels

  SAWYER

  IMBRA

  JUBY

  LLOYD

  FENN MARK III

  FENN MARK IV

  FENN MARK VI

GIN TRAPS ARE ILLEGAL

Catch alive cage and box traps are not restricted although may require certain obligations for the provision of food, water and shade.

SNARES - SELF LOCKING ARE ILLEGAL (see page 312).

POISONS -GAS *Agriculture Act* 1947 and the *Agricultural Act (Scotland)* 1948 restrict the use of poison gas to animals living in holes, i.e. foxes, rabbits, rats and moles.

  The poisoning of animals and birds is generally illegal except in the following instances:

  1. Against rats and mice.

  2. Against moles (strychnine may be used under Ministry permit only).

3. Against grey squirrels (only Warfarin may be used in certain areas and to be fed from specially designed hoppers). May not be used in Scotland. The use of Warfarin is clearly defined in the *Grey Squirrels (Warfarin) Order,* 1973 made under the *Agriculture (Miscellaneous Provisions) Act,*1972, available from H.M.S.O.

Other Acts of Parliament relating to the use of poisons are:

Protection of Animals Act, 1911.

Protection of Animals (Scotland) Act, 1912.

Animals (Cruel Poisons) Act, 1962.

Agriculture (Miscellaneous Provisions) Act, 1972.

Protection of Animals Act, 1911, Section 8

POISON

It is an offence to knowingly put, place, cause, procure or be party to placing in or upon land or buildings, poison, poisonous fluid or edible matter. There is a defence to this. (see page 311).

ANIMALS (CRUEL POISONS) ACT, 1962

It is an offence to use prohibited or restricted poisons. Certain exceptions are made for insects, invertebrates, rats, mice and other small ground vermin. Also for gassing rabbits or foxes. It is an offence to use an infected rabbit to spread myxomatosis.

SPRING TRAPS

Section 8 Pests Act, 1954.

It is an offence for any person to use or permit the use of a spring trap *not* approved or to sell, offer for sale or possess any spring trap for an unlawful purpose.

Approved spring traps for rabbits may only be placed in rabbit holes.

Spring traps may be baited with non-poisonous baits if required.

Spring traps should be placed under cover.

SECTION 10 PROTECTION OF ANIMALS ACT, 1911

It is an offence for any person who sets, or causes to be set, any spring trap for the purpose of catching, or placed where it is likely to catch, a hare or rabbit and who fails to inspect it at reasonable intervals and at least once a day between sunrise and sunset.

Wildlife and Countryside Act, 1981 - Animals

SECTION 9

It is an offence to intentionally kill, injure, take or possess an animal included in Schedule 5. (see page 308).

It is also an offence to intentionally damage, destroy or obstruct access to shelter, etc., or to disturb an animal (included in Schedule 5) while in occupation.

Exceptions are made if a disabled animal is taken to tend and then released. Also if an animal is severely injured and there is no chance of recovery it may be lawfully killed. Also included is action that may be required by the Minister of Agriculture Fisheries and Food to prevent damage to crops, etc. or orders made under the *Animal Health Act,* 1981.

N.B. Defence is only effective if in possession of a licence or an application has been made previously.

SECTION 11

It is an offence to set in position any trap, snare, electrical device, poisonous, poisoned or stupefying substance calculated to cause bodily injury to any wild animal included in Schedule 6. (see page 308).

(It will be a defence, however, if it is shown that reasonable precautions were taken to prevent such an occurrence when such articles were being lawfully used to kill or take any other wild animal and that the action was in the interest of conservation, agriculture, forestry, fisheries or public health.)

Included in Section 11 are the use of the following:

a. Automatic/Semi-automatic weapons capable of holding more than two rounds in the magazine

b. Device for illuminating the target

c. Sighting device for night shooting

d. Artificial light, mirror or dazzling device

e. Any gas or smoke

f. Sound recording for use as a decoy

g. Mechanically propelled vehicle

h. Any net.

It is an offence for any person to set in position, or kill or take any wild animal, self locking snares or to use a bow, cross bow, or explosive. Or to use as a decoy any live bird or animal in order to kill or take any wild animal.

It is an offence for any person to set in position any snare, of such a nature and so placed, calculated to cause bodily injury to any wild animal coming into contact and while the snare is in position fails without reasonable excuse to inspect it or cause it to be inspected at least once every day.

Badger Act, 1973 as amended by the Wildlife and Countryside Act, 1981.

SECTION 1

It is an offence if any person wilfully kills, injures or takes any badger or attempts to do so.

Exception may be made if action is necessary to prevent serious damage to property, crops, livestock, etc. and then only if a Section 9 licence has been applied for or determined.

SECTION 2

It is an offence to cruelly ill treat any badger, to use badger tongs or to dig for any badger unless permitted by the *Wildlife and Countryside Act,* 1981, even then only certain firearms may be used to kill a badger.

SECTION 3

It is an offence to possess, control, sell or offer for sale any live badgers.

Exceptions may be made for badgers that have accidentally been injured or that have been bred in captivity.

Wildlife and Countryside Act 1981 - Birds

Wild birds are divided into different categories covered by Schedules, and some are defined as Game birds.

SECTION 1

It is an offence to intentionally kill, injure or take any wild bird or take, damage or destroy the nest or eggs of any wild bird.

SECTION 1 (2)

It is an offence to possess or control a wild bird (dead or alive) or an egg or parts of the bird or egg.

SECTION 1 (5)

It is an offence to disturb a Schedule 1 wild bird (see note below) while building a nest or in, on or near a nest containing eggs or young, or to disturb the young of these birds.

N.B. This includes birds in Schedule 1 at any time and birds in Schedule 1 Part 2 and Schedule 2 Part 1 during the close season.

SECTION 2

It is an offence to take or kill a wild bird included in Schedule 1 Part 2 and Schedule 2 Part 1 under special protection during the period of a statutory ban.

It is **not** an offence to take or kill a Schedule 2 Part 1 bird outside the close season nor for an authorised person to kill or take a Schedule 2 Part 2 wild bird or its nest or its eggs at any time.

A person is not guilty of an offence if he is acting as a requirement of the Minister of Agriculture, Fisheries and Food or the Secretary of State. Nor is he guilty of an offence if the bird was disabled and taken to treat and release when fit, if the bird was killed because it was seriously disabled with no reasonable chance of recovery, or if the unlawful act was an incidental result of a lawful operation which could not reasonably be avoided.

The taking of wild mallard eggs by an authorised person for the purpose of hatching and releasing back into the wild is permitted by a licence issued by the Department of the Environment.

SECTION 5

It is an offence to set in position the following articles of such a nature and so placed that they are calculated to cause bodily injury to any wild bird coming into contact.

Spring trap, gin trap, snare, hook and line, electrical device or poisonous, poisoned or stupefying substance. Also included are nets, baited boards and bird lime or similar substances.

It is an offence to kill or take any wild bird, using a bow or cross bow, explosive (other than firearm ammunition) gas or smoke, chemical wetting agent, artificial light, mirror or dazzling device. Device for illuminating target, sighting device for night shooting or a shot gun with a barrel having an internal diameter at the muzzle in excess of 1 3/4 inches. Also included are automatic/semi automatic weapons capable of holding more than two rounds in the magazine.

It is an offence to use as a decoy to kill or take any wild bird, any sound recording or live bird or animal that is tethered, secured, blind, maimed or injured. Also to use any mechanically propelled vehicle in immediate pursuit of a wild bird in order to kill or to take it.

Exceptions are made for an authorised person to use a cage trap or net to take Schedule 2 Part 2 birds and to use a cage trap or net to take any game bird *for breeding.* Also included is the allowance that birds may be accidentally killed or injured by traps, etc., which have been lawfully set for the control of wild animals in the interests of agriculture, fisheries, forestry, conservation, etc. Reasonable precautions must have been taken to prevent injury to wild birds.

SECTION 8

It is an offence for any person to arrange, take part in, receive money, etc., for any event where captive birds are liberated by hand or other means to be shot immediately after liberation or for the owner or occupier to permit the use of his property for such an event.

Should game birds or wildfowl be liberated immediately prior to being driven over guns to be shot, all concerned (beaters, guns, assistants, etc.) would be liable to prosecution.

THEFT

Theft Act 1968 - Section 25

It is an offence for any person when not at his place of abode to have with him any article for use in the course of or in connection with any burglary, theft or cheat.

Any person may arrest any person who is committing, or with reasonable cause is suspected of committing, this offence.

Vagrancy Act 1824 - Section 4

If a person is found in or upon a dwelling house, warehouse, coach house, stable, out house or in an enclosed yard, garden or area for any unlawful purpose he may be arrested.

Powers of arrest are as above.

If a person is armed with an offensive weapon or instrument with intent to commit an arrestable offence or commits an arrestable offence he may be arrested.

Powers of arrest are as above.

TRAFFIC
Road Traffic Act 1972 - Section 35

It is an offence to promote or take part in trials of motor vehicles on a footpath or bridleway* unless authorised by the local authority and given the consent of the land owner.

SECTION 36

It is an offence without lawful authority to drive a motor vehicle on to common land, moorland, land of any other description or roadway being a public footpath or bridleway.*

Exception is made within 15 yards of a road for the purpose of parking.

Highways Act 1980 - Section 148

It is an offence to deposit anything whatsoever on a highway causing interruption to any user of the highway. (This may be interpreted to include mud, etc.) Dumping within 15 feet of the carriageway is also prohibited and includes dung, compost, or other material for dressing the land as well as rubbish.

Litter Act 1983 - Section 1

It is an offence to deposit litter in a place to which the public have free access (this may be interpreted to include footpaths, bridleways* and lay-bys) unless authorised.

*For definition of footpath and bridleway see page 335.

BURNING

The Heather and Grass Etc. (Burning) Regulations 1986. England and Wales

(Heather, rough grass, bracken, gorse and vaccinium)

It is an offence between 15 April and 1 October; and additionally on land which is not an upland area, between 31 March and 16 April or between 30 September and 1 November to burn heather, grass etc. unless a licence is obtained from the Minister of Agriculture, Fisheries and Food (England) or the Secretary of State (Wales).

Heather and grass etc. may be burnt outside the above dates but only under the following conditions:

1. Burning must be carried out between sunrise and sunset.

2. A sufficient number of people and equipment must be available to control and regulate burning during the entire period of operation.

3. Precautions must be taken before commencing and during the entire period of operation to prevent damage or injury to any adjacent land, or to any person or thing whatsoever on that land.

4. At least 24 hours and not more than 72 hours notice in writing needs to be given to owners or occupiers of adjacent land giving full details of date, time and place at which, and the extent of the area on which it is intended to burn.

STRAW AND STUBBLE BURNING

Legal controls are through byelaws adopted by District Councils concerning the burning of straw and stubble. Each contravention carries stiff penalties. A general summary of typical byelaws in force are:

1. Never burn where damage or annoyance to the public may occur.

2. Never burn at weekends or Bank Holidays.

3. Never burn if the weather is unsuitable.

4. Always burn against the wind if possible.

5. Never light a fire before sunrise, or within an hour of sunset.

6. Never burn without at least two people to supervise each fire.

7. A firebreak (clear of straw with either 5 metres ploughed or the entire strip cultivated) must be created between area to be burned and other features. For buildings, standing crops, machinery, etc., this must be 25

metres wide and for others such as hedges, trees, telegraph poles, it must be 15 metres.

8. Straw should be cleared from beneath any overhead installations (power lines, etc.).

9. The fire brigade, neighbours and District Council may need to be informed.

10. Fire fighting equipment must be available (at least 500 litres of water and five fire beating implements).

11. The block to be burned should not exceed 10 hectares and is at least 150 metres away from any other being burned.

12. There is full insurance cover.

13. Ashes must be incorporated within 36 hours.

14. Always ensure that the ashes are fully extinguished before nightfall. A fire should not be lit if the wind exceeds force 3 (8-12 mph) or if the wind will create a smoke hazard on roads or to local residents.

The Highways Act 1980

SECTIONS 131 and 161

It is an offence to start a fire within 50 feet of thee centre of the road so as to injure, interrupt or endanger passers by or damage the Highway.

The Code of Practice for straw and stubble burning advises that no fire should be started within 100 metres of a motorway or dual carriageway.

The Clean Air Act 1956

Provides that action may be taken against anyone who allows smoke (or smuts emitted by smoke) to endanger public health or cause a nuisance.

DOGS AND LIVESTOCK

Control of Dogs Act 1930

Exempts dogs being used for sporting purposes or for the destruction of vermin from wearing a collar with the owner's name and address on it.

Guard Dogs Act 1975

A person shall not use or permit the use of a guard dog at any premises (not agricultural land or dwelling house) unless a handler is present on the premises and he controls the dog at all times and warning notices are exhibited at each entrance to the premises.

Dog Licence Act 1959

It is an offence to keep a dog without a licence.*

The Dogs (Protection of Livestock) Act 1953

SECTION 1

If a dog worries (i.e. attacks or chases in a way likely to cause injury or suffering, abortion or loss of or diminution in their produce) livestock (see definition, page 336) on any agricultural land (arable, grazing land, meadow or land used for poultry/pig farming, market gardens, allotments, nursery grounds or orchard) the owner or person in charge is committing an offence.

It is a civil wrong to kill or injure a person's dog; to kill or injure a dog could therefore lead to the payment of damages for the dog owner. Defences are provided by:

a) The necessity to protect livestock and police are given notice of a shooting within 48 hours.

b) The necessity to shoot the dog in self defence.

c) Where a dog has attacked domestic animals which are not livestock and no other means to prevent the attack were available.

If a dog (does not apply to working dogs or hounds) is at large in a field or enclosure containing sheep, the owner or person in charge is committing an offence.

Animals Act 1971

SECTION 7

If livestock that is not under control strays onto any land it may be detained by the occupier of the land unless a court orders its return. Right to detain ends after 48 hours unless the police and owners are notified or the livestock is claimed by the owner who offers sufficient money to recompense the occupier.

A claim could be made in respect of the damage caused and/or for the cost of tending the straying livestock.

* Now rescinded (1988) so no licence is required.

The Highways Act 1980

SECTION 155

This Act deals with penalties in connection with straying animals.

If horses, cattle, sheep, goats or swine are found straying onto the highway at any time their keeper is guilty of an offence. A person found guilty of this offence may also be liable to pay any expenses incurred in the removal and upkeep of such straying animals.

FIREARMS
The Firearms Act 1968

Describes the different types of weapons.

A RIFLE

A SHOTGUN is a smooth bore gun with a barrel not less than 24 inches in length and not being an air gun.

AN AIR WEAPON is an air rifle, gun or pistol and does not require a firearms certificate unless it exceeds a specified power output.

NAIL GUNS, ALARM GUNS, AND CROSSBOWS are not considered to be firearms.

SHOTGUNS A shotgun certificate is required by law to possess a shotgun. If the barrels are less than 24" in length a firearm certificate is required. Under the following circumstances a shotgun certificate is **NOT** required:

a. A shotgun is borrowed from the occupier of private premises (including land) and is used in his presence on his premises.

b. A shotgun belonging to someone else is used on artificial targets at a time and place approved by the local chief officer of Police.

c. A shotgun is used by a person visiting Great Britain from abroad for a total of not more than 30 days in 12 months.

d. A Northern Ireland Firearm certificate for a shotgun is possessed by the user.

e. If a shotgun is being carried for another person in connection with sporting purposes.

f. To purchase ammunition (cartridges) for a shotgun.

The Firearms Act 1968

SECTION 2

It is an offence to possess/purchase/acquire a shotgun without holding a valid shotgun certificate.

There is **no** lower age limit set at which a person may apply for and obtain a shotgun certificate. The issuing of a certificate is usually straight-forward. The following restrictions are made on the use of shotguns by young people:

1. It is an offence to make a gift of a shotgun or ammunition to a person under 15.

2. A person under 15 may **not** have with him an assembled shotgun unless under the supervision of a person over the age of 21 or unless the gun is so covered that it cannot be fired.

3. Persons over the age of 15 may use a shotgun providing they hold a valid shotgun certificate.

4. A person under 17 may not purchase or hire a shotgun or ammunition although he may be given or lent one.

Wildlife and Countryside Act 1981

PROHIBITED METHODS OF KILLING - SECTION 5

It is unlawful to kill any wild or game bird using a shotgun with a barrel having an internal diameter at the muzzle in excess of 1 3/4 inches or using an automatic or semi-automatic weapon holding more than two rounds of ammunition in the magazine.

N.B. An automatic or semi-automatic weapon capable of holding more than two rounds in the magazine may be used to shoot animals which are **not** included in Schedules 5 and 6, i.e. rabbits and hares, etc. (see page 308).

Firearms

A firearms certificate is issued by the police only when a good reason can be proved for the need to use a rifle. Stringent conditions are imposed on the use and storage and the purchase and possession of ammunition which cannot be obtained without a firearm certificate. Each firearm owned must be listed on the owner's certificate and if the rifle is used by another person it must also be listed on his firearm certificate.

Any change of address, theft or loss of a rifle or a firearm certificate must be reported immediately.

Firearms Act 1968

SECTION 1

It is an offence to possess or to purchase or to acquire a Section 1 Firearm (see note*) without holding a valid firearm certificate. It is also an offence to purchase/possess or acquire any ammunition without holding a valid certificate or to purchase/possess or acquire ammunition of a type or quantity not authorised on the certificate.

This requirement applies to every firearm except:

a. A shotgun (smooth bore gun with a barrel not less than 24" in length);

b. An air weapon.

This requirement also applies to ammunition except:

a. Cartridges containing five or more shot, none of which exceeds .36 inch in diameter;

b. Ammunition for an air weapon;

c. Blank cartridges not more than 1 inch in diameter.

Restrictions

Restrictions are imposed on the use of rifles by persons under 17.

1. A firearm certificate will not be issued to any person under 14.

2. A person under 14 may not be in the possession of a firearm or ammunition, except at an approved club, shooting gallery, etc.

3. It is an offence for any person to make a gift to, or lend any firearm or ammunition to a person under the age of 14.

4. A person under 17 may borrow or accept as a gift, a firearm or ammunition providing he is the holder of a valid firearm certificate. It is an offence for any person under 17 to purchase or hire any firearm or ammunition.

It is an offence to sell or let on hire any firearm or ammunition to a person under the age of 17.

*NOTE: Firearms Act 1968 includes: Rifles, revolvers, pistols, humane killers, grenades and bombs to be fired from a firearm, flare signal pen, gas guns, prohibited weapons, Very pistols, sound and flash moderators, components, working parts and ammunition.

Exceptions to Firearm Certificate Requirements

SECTION 7 - POLICE PERMIT

A person who has obtained a permit from the chief officer of police for the area in which he resides may possess a firearm and ammunition without holding a certificate under this Act.

It is an offence to give false information to obtain a permit.

SECTION 8 - Authorised dealing with firearms

A registered firearms dealer or a person employed by him may possess, purchase or acquire a firearm or ammunition without holding a certificate in the ordinary course of his business.

It is not an offence to part with possession of any firearm or ammunition other than for sale, hire, gift or loan to a person entitled under this Act to possess a firearm or ammunition without holding a certificate.

Nor to return to another a shotgun which he has lawfully repaired, tested or proved for another.

SECTION 11

A person carrying a firearm or ammunition on behalf of another person holding a firearm certificate does not need a certificate to have in his possession that firearm or ammunition under the instructions from and for the use of that other person for sporting purposes only.

A person possessing a firearm at an athletics meeting for the purpose of starting races at that meeting does not need a certificate.

A person who is a member of an approved rifle club, miniature rifle club or cadet corps may possess a firearm and ammunition when engaged as a member of that club, or in connection with, drill or target practice.

A certificate is not needed by a person in charge of a miniature rifle range or shooting gallery (where no firearms are used other than air weapons or miniature rifles not exceeding .23 inch calibre) to possess, purchase or acquire such weapons and ammunition, nor for a person to use such weapons at a range or gallery.

Legislation concerning firearms is currently being reviewed.

Air Weapons

Firearms Act 1968

SECTIONS 23 & 24

Although no certificate is required for the possession and use of air weapons, certain restrictions are imposed on their use by young persons. It also constitutes an offence to be in possession of an air weapon under certain conditions (see page 324).

Persons under 14 cannot buy, hire, or be given an air weapon or ammunition, but may use one on private premises if supervised at all times by a person over 21. The ammunition used must fall within the confines of the private premises.

Persons over 14 but under 17 cannot buy or hire an air weapon, but can receive one as a gift. The air weapon may be used unsupervised on private property providing permission has been obtained.

Exceptions are made for the use of air weapons at approved clubs, shooting galleries, etc.

It is an offence to make a gift of an air weapon or ammunition for an air weapon to a person under the age of 14, or part with the possession of, except where that person is not prohibited from having an air weapon or ammunition.

SECTION 19

It is an offence for any person without lawful authority or reasonable excuse to have in a public place a loaded shotgun, loaded air weapon or any other firearm with ammunition for that firearm, whether loaded or not.

Any person may arrest any person who is committing or with reasonable cause is suspected to be committing this offence. This does not, however, apply in the case of air weapons when only a police officer may arrest the offender.

SECTION 20

It is an offence for any person to have with him any firearm (this includes shotguns and air weapons) when he enters on land or water or in a building as a trespasser without reasonable excuse.

Power of arrest as above.

Any person may apprehend any person who is drunk in possession of any loaded firearm.

A valid shotgun certificate does not give a person a lawful authority to have with him a loaded shotgun in a public place.

Highways Act 1980

SECTION 161

It is an offence without lawful authority or reasonable excuse to discharge any firearm within 50 feet of the centre of the highway the consequence of which may injure, endanger or interrupt the user of the highway.

Wildlife and Countryside Act 1981

SECTION 5

It is an offence to use a cross bow to take or kill any wild bird or game bird (also animals).

A police officer has the power to stop, search and arrest any person who he has reasonable cause to suspect of committing or having committed an offence.

Gun Barrel Proof Acts 1868 to 1978*

It is an offence to offer for sale an unproven firearm or one which has been materially weakened by the enlargement of the bore since it was last proved and therefore invalidating the proof marks.

There are severe penalties imposed in the form of heavy fines, imprisonment or both for any breach of the laws concerning firearms.

All firearms should be looked after in a responsible manner. Great care should be taken when in use and when not in use firearms should be stored securely, preferably separate from the ammunition. Certificates must be signed in ink immediately they are issued and should also be kept in a safe place.

Any change of conditions, name, address, theft or loss should be notified to the police immediately.

*These Acts provide for penalties for offences in relation to stamping and marking of barrels, and dealing by way of sale or exchange or export, with small arms the barrels of which have not been proved as the Act requires.

GAME LAWS
Shooting Season - Dates inclusive

GROUSE 12 August - 10 December

PTARMIGAN 12 August - 10 December

BLACKGAME 20 August - 10 December

CAPERCAILLIE 1 October - 31 January

COMMON SNIPE 12 August - 31 January

WOODCOCK 1 October - 31 January

(1 September - 31 January Scotland)

ENGLISH PARTRIDGE 1 September - 1 February

FRENCH PARTRIDGE 1 September - 1 February

PHEASANT 1 October - 1 February

A game licence is required to take, kill or pursue the species listed above. None of them may be shot on Sundays or Christmas day in Great Britain.

Ground Game (Rabbits and Hares only)
Ground Game Act 1880

There is no close season for hares and rabbits except for the following:

Hares may not be taken on Sundays or Christmas Day;

Hares may not be offered for sale during the months of March to July inclusive.

Hare Preservation Act 1892
Criminal Justice Act 1982

Ground game may only be taken from 11th December to 31st March on moorland and unenclosed non-arable land. However, this close season does not apply if this land is less than 25 acres and adjoining arable land.

The occupier of moorland or unenclosed land is permitted to take ground game between 1st September and 10th December.

A game licence is required to kill hares, although there are certain exceptions.

The owner of the land has the right to take or kill game. These rights may be sold to an individual or to a group, i.e. a syndicate.

The rights may be retained by the owner even when the land itself has been leased out, but if no agreement has been drawn up the game rights will automatically pass to the tenant.

In some cases the game rights may be transferred to the tenant.

So far as a gamekeeper is concerned the situation over game rights on all of the estate should be clarified from the beginning. Difficulties may arise when small parcels of land may have been sold off, together with houses, to private buyers who may very well be anti-shooting. The game rights should be retained by the estate wherever possible in such circumstances.

Ground Game Act 1880

Only rabbits and hares are classed as ground game. Even if the owner has retained the shooting rights for himself, the occupier also possesses the right to kill the ground game due to the serious damage that may be caused to crops and timber. Thus, it can arise that two people have the right to shoot ground game.

Restrictions are imposed on the occupier as to the persons he may authorise to shoot the ground game: they are:

a) One or more members of the occupier's household resident on the land in his occupation;

b) one or more people in the occupier's service;

c) Any other person bona fide employed by the occupier for reward in the taking or the destruction of ground game.

The right of the occupier to shoot ground game is incidental to his occupation and he cannot be divested of it.

NIGHT SHOOTING

Under *Section 6* night shooting is permitted only under the following conditions. It must be done by the land owner, the occupier or person authorised by him (see above) or a person entitled by the owner to take the ground game.

It is advisable to notify the police and neighbours of the intention to go night shooting.

With the above exceptions, there is no right to shoot ground game at night or to use poison or spring traps (except those placed within rabbit holes) to take or kill ground game.

Game Act 1831 & Game Licence Act 1860

A game licence is required for the following:

1. Taking game (e.g. catching in a trap or snare with the intention of keeping or killing);

2. Killing game (accidental killing is not an offence, but if it is followed by taking away then it becomes an offence);

3. Using any dog, net, gun, etc. for the purpose of searching for, pursuing, taking or killing game;

4. Pursuing game, or siding or assisting in any manner in the taking, killing or pursuing of game by any means whatsoever. (Loaders, beaters, pickers up, etc. will generally be exempted from the need of a game licence).

The *Game Act 1831* includes hares, pheasants, partridges, grouse, heath or moor game and black game. The *Game Licences Act 1860* adds deer (see page 332/7), rabbits, woodcock and snipe to the previous list (see page 337).

Game Licences are available from the Post Office and are issued to cover the whole year or only certain seasons of the year.

A Gamekeepers licence is issued annually on August 1st and should be obtained by his employer. This exempts his gamekeeper from the need to purchase a game licence on his own land. It may be transferred from 'A' to 'B' in the same employment.

A game licence is not required by the occupier or the persons he has authorised to take ground game, who are also entitled to sell it.

Game Dealers Act 1831

A person who purchases, sells or deals in game must obtain a licence.

Exceptions are made for the sale of game consumed on the premises and the authorised selling of hares.

It is an offence for a game dealer to purchase game from a person not licenced to kill or sell game.

POACHING

Poaching - Night

Night Poaching Acts 1828 & 1844

SECTION 1

It is an offence for any person by night* to take or destroy game, rabbits or hares on any land, open or enclosed or any public highway, road, path or side thereof.

It is an offence for any person by night to unlawfully enter or be on any open or enclosed land with any gun, net, engine or other instrument (can include a dog) for the purpose of taking or destroying game.

If three or more persons are involved in poaching and any one of them is armed,* Section 9 of the 1828 Act provides that each and every one of them is guilty of a further offence. If any person offers violence towards a gamekeeper or other authorised person he may be liable to a specially severe penalty.

The gamekeeper, (a gamekeeper employed by persons having the shooting rights but not owning or occupying the land, does not have the power of arrest under offences under Section 1, 2 or 9 of the *Night Poaching Act 1818*) owner or occupier of the land or other servant may lawfully apprehend any person but not search him or seize his equipment or guns.

Section 4 Game Laws (Amendment) Act 1960

Provides the police with the power to arrest a suspect and to search him and seize any equipment he may have in his possession.

*See page 336 for definition of night.

*"Armed" means with a gun, crossbow, firearm, bludgeon or any other offensive weapon.

Poaching - Day
Game Act 1831

SECTION 3

It is an offence to take or pursue game on a Sunday, Christmas Day or during the close season (see page 325). Any person commits this offence who uses a gun, dog, net or other engine for the purpose of taking or killing game on these days.

SECTION 30

It is an offence to trespass by entering or being upon any land (including rivers and lakes) in the daytime in search or pursuit of (Live) game, rabbits or hares.

The entry on the land must be actual. If a person shoots or sends his dog from the highway, the highway itself will be deemed as being the property of the adjacent landowner.

SECTION 31

A person found committing the above offence by a person who has the right to take game (owner, occupier, gamekeeper or other authorised person) may be required to quit the land forthwith and to give his full name and address. If, after this request, he refuses to give, or gives a false address, refuses to leave the land or returns to it, he may be apprehended.

SECTION 36

When a person is found committing the offence of day or night poaching and is in possession of game recently killed, the owner or occupier of the land, their gamekeepers and servants may seize that game.

On failure to obtain a conviction the articles seized must be returned to the defendants.

Poaching Prevention Act 1862

SECTION 2

Provides the police with the power to stop on any land, street, highway or public place and search any person or article suspected of poaching or vehicle used. He may seize any articles that may have been used (with the exception of dogs and ferrets) and he may summons the offender although he does not have the power of arrest. On failure to obtain a conviction the articles must be returned to the defendants.

Occupiers Liability Act 1984

SECTION 1

A property owner has a duty towards a trespasser if he knows or has reasonable grounds to believe that the trespasser is in the vicinity of any danger due to the state of the premises or to things done or omitted to be done on them, e.g. not having dangerous "traps" on the premises.

DEER

Close Seasons for Deer (inclusive)

SPECIES	SEX	ENGLAND & WALES -	SCOTLAND
RED	STAGS	1 May - 31 July	21 Oct - 30 June
	HINDS	1 March - 31 Oct	16 Feb - 20 Oct
FALLOW	BUCK	1 May - 31 July	1 May - 31 July
	DOE	1 March - 31 Oct	16 Feb - 20 Oct
ROE	BUCK	1 Nov 31 March	21 Oct 31 March
	DOE	1 March 31 Oct	1 April - 20 Oct
SIKA	STAGS	1 May - 31 July	21 Oct - 30 June
	HINDS	1 March - 31 Oct	16 Feb - 20 Oct
RED/SIKA HYBRIDS	STAGS		21 Oct - 30 June Scotland
	HINDS		16 Feb - 20 Oct Only

The British Deer Society have recommended that a close season from 1 March to 31 October for both buck and does is introduced for Muntjac and Chinese Water Deer.

Deer Act 1963

SECTION 1

It is an offence to take or wilfully kill any red, fallow, roe or sika deer at night or during the close season (see page 330).

Deer Act 1987 (England and Wales Only)

This is an act that makes it lawful for deer kept on deer farms to be killed during a close season.

Any person who, by way of business, keeps deer on land enclosed by a deer-proof barrier for the production of meat or other foodstuffs or skins or other by-products or as breeding stock and those deer are conspicuously marked in such a way as to identify them as deer kept by that person, the killing of any of those deer by that person, or by any servant or agent of that person authorised by him for that purpose shall not constitute an offence against Section I of *The Deer Act* 1963.

SECTION 3

It is an offence to set in position traps, snares, poisoned or stupefying bait of such a nature and so placed as to be calculated to cause bodily injury to any deer coming into contact.

This includes nets, arrows, spears, shooting from any type of vehicle, any type of air weapon, any shotgun (except if the killing is an act of mercy or in some cases where a S.16 licence has been granted) or any rifle less than a .240 (not Scotland).

This law is open to some abuse and amendments are being sought to close any existing loopholes.

Automatic rifles are banned, but the semi-automatic or self- loading rifle is still permitted. Bullets must be soft or hollow nosed.

Normal telescopic sights are permitted, but not with infra-red sights.

Deer Act 1980

SECTION 1

It is an offence for any person to search for and pursue deer with the intention of or attempting to kill any deer or remove the carcase of any deer without the consent of the owner, occupier or other lawful authority.

Game Act 1831

SECTION 36

(see page 329) applies for deer with the exception that only a police officer may seize the deer or carcase.

Recently there has been an increase in the penalties for the unlawful taking, killing and injuring of deer. Breach of the firearms order may result in severe penalties or fines and/or imprisonment assessed on every deer killed or taken. Courts have been empowered to cancel firearm or shotgun certificates for those convicted of the above crimes.

Deer Act 1980

SECTION 3

States that only a dealer licenced to sell venison may handle deer and records must be kept of deer and the details of when and from whom they were bought.

Any dealer convicted of an offence connected with the illegal taking of deer may be disqualified from holding a licence.

Game Licences Act 1860

SECTION 5

A game licence is not required to take or kill deer in enclosed land, with the permission of, or by the direction of, the owner of occupier of the land.

"Enclosed land" means land used for farming and enclosed by normal agricultural use.

FISH

Theft Act 1968

SECTION 32

It is an offence to unlawfully take or destroy or attempt to take or destroy any fish in water which is private property or in which there is a private right of fishery.

Any person may arrest any person who is, or who with reasonable cause is, suspected to be taking destroying or attempting to take or destroy any fish in water which is private property or private right of fishing and may seize any article used to take or destroy fish. This includes angling at night but there is no power to arrest any person unlawfully angling during day time.

CLOSE SEASONS FOR SALMON, TROUT AND GRAYLING

Every Water Authority is under a statutory duty to fix an annual close season for salmon and brown trout within its area. These byelaws vary throughout the country but invariably include the winter months. Subject to variations made by local water authorities the close season for grayling is the period between the 14 March and 16 June.

Salmon and Fisheries Act 1975

SECTIONS 1-5

PROHIBITED METHODS OF FISHING

Salmon, Trout and Freshwater fish

1. Firearms, stone or other missile

2. Cross line (baited line from bank to bank)

3. Spear or gaff (unless used to land a fish already caught on a hook and line)

Other instrument for foul hooking (to deliberately hook a fish in its side)

4. Light

5. Set line (baited line left unattended)

6. Otter lath or jack (small boat, board or stick etc. for running out lures)
   Wire or snare

7. Fish roe.

Salmon and Migratory Trout

1. Seine or draft net longer than 3/4 the width of the water

2. Net less than 2" knot to knot on each side of square excepting a landing net

3. Placing 2 or more such nets close together.

Any fish (in inland waters or up to 6 nautical miles from the coast)

1. Explosive

2. Poison

3. Noxious substance

4. Electrical device.

The prohibition of the use of explosives, poisons, noxious substances or electrical devices does not apply to the use by any person with the written permission of the Water Authority for the area, for a scientific purpose for the intention of protecting, improving or replacing stocks of fish.

SECTION 25 Unlicenced Fishing

Water authorities are legally obliged to control fishing by licencing and close seasons.

Salmon and Freshwater Fisheries Act 1975
SECTION 27

It is an offence in any place where fishing is regulated by licence to fish for or take fish without a licence, by using means prohibited by licence or contrary to licence conditions.

A fishing licence entitles the person to whom it is granted to use an instrument specified in the licence to fish for any fish of a description in an area and in the period specified in the licence.

SECTION 30

It is an offence to introduce fish spawn into inland waters without written consent of the water authority.

SECTION 31

A water bailiff (appointed by the water authority or the M.A.F.F.) may enter land to investigate dam, fishing weir or mill dam, fixed engine or obstruction or artificial water course.

He may also examine and seize any items including vessels or vehicles that he suspects of being used for unlawful fishing. Refusal to allow the Water Bailiff to enter and search or examine, or obstruction of the water bailiff, is an offence itself.

SECTION 34

If any person is found at night intending to or illegally taking, or possessing a prohibited instrument to capture salmon, trout, fresh water fish and eels, the water bailiff may seize the person and hand him over to the police.

SECTION 35

Gives a water bailiff power to require the production of a licence and the name and address of the suspect.

DEFINITIONS OF TERMS USED

AUTHORISED PERSON

a) The owner or occupier, or any person authorised by the owner or occupier of the land, on which the action authorised is taken;

b) Any person authorised in writing by the local authority for the area in which the action authorised is taken.

BRIDLEWAY

A right of way on foot and a right of way on horseback or leading a horse with or without a right to drive animals of any description along the highway. Subject to local authority orders and byelaws there is also a right of way for cyclists but they must give way to other users. *Section 30 Countryside Act 1968).*

COMMON

Privately owned land over which the common rights (grazing, firewood, etc.) have been granted. It does not necessarily give the right of access to the general public although many do.

FOOTPATH

A highway over which there is right of way on foot only.

FIREARM

Includes shotguns, rifles and air weapons.

FIREARM CERTIFICATE

Certificate required for rifles and certain other weapons (see page 321).

GAME

Grouse, ptarmigan, black game, English and French partridge, pheasants, hares. Woodcock, snipe and capercaillie are generally classified as game and rabbits and deer are included in certain instances.

LIVESTOCK

Defined in the *Animals Act 1971* Section II, includes:

Cattle, horses, asses, mules, hinnies, sheep, pigs, goats, poultry, deer not in a wild state and also, while in captivity, pheasants, partridges and grouse. 'Poultry' means the domestic varieties of fowls - turkeys, geese, ducks, guinea-fowls, pigeons, peacocks and quail, chickens, etc.

M.A.F.F.

Ministry of Agriculture, Fisheries and Food.

NIGHT

The period between 1 hour after sunset and 1 hour before sunrise local time.

PROOF OF FIREARM

The compulsory testing of any firearm (except air weapons) to ensure its safety.

S 16 LICENCE

Licence granted by M.A.F.F. under the *Wildlife and Countryside Act 1981* to destroy certain species where it is necessary to protect livestock, crops, vegetables, fruit, growing timber and fisheries from serious damage.

SHOTGUN CERTIFICATE

Certificate required for the use of a shotgun of any size bore.

TRESPASS

Unauthorised entry by a person who has no permission from the owner or occupier of the land. If a person sends his dog or shoots onto land from the highway, the highway itself will be considered to be the property of the adjacent land owner in the case of day poaching.

VEHICLE

Mechanically powered, includes those used on the land, water, or in the air.

List of game birds and animals included in various poaching offences and licences

GROUND GAME ACT 1880

Hares and rabbits.

GAME ACT 1831

Pheasants, partridge, grouse, black game, moor game, hares.

NIGHT POACHING ACTS 1828 and 1844

Pheasant, partridge, grouse, black game, moor game, hares and rabbits.

POACHING PREVENTION ACT 1862

Pheasant,* partridge,* grouse,*, black game,* moor game,* hares, rabbits, woodcock, snipe (*includes eggs of species marked).

GAME ACT 1831 TRESPASSING IN DAY TIME

Pheasant, partridge, grouse, black game, moor game, hares, rabbits, woodcock, snipe.

GAME LICENCE ACT 1860 - KILLING OF GAME

Pheasant, partridge, grouse, black game, moor game, hares, rabbits, woodcock, snipe, deer.

GAME INCLUDED IN GAME DEALERS LICENCE

Pheasant, partridge, grouse, black game, moor game, hares

AGRICULTURAL HOLDINGS ACT 1948

Species where compensation is payable to a tenant for damage to his crops. Pheasant, partridge, grouse, black game, deer.

ADDRESSES OF HER MAJESTY'S STATIONERY OFFICES:
P.O. Box 569, London SE1 9NH.
13A Castle Street, Edinburgh EH2 3AR.
Brazenose Street, Manchester M60 8AS.
Southey House, Wine Street, Bristol BS1 2BQ.
258 Broad Street, Birmingham B1 2HE.
80 Chichester Street, Belfast BT1 4JY.

Detailed copies of individual laws are obtainable from H.M.S.O. at the above addresses.

19
Do's and Don't's Out Shooting
Beaters
Pickers Up
Guns

19.1 Beaters on the way to a shoot

Beaters Do's

DO Arrive punctually.

DO Come suitably dress, i.e. adequate footwear and water-proof clothing.

DO Bring a stick - used for dislodging pheasants from cover, tapping to make them run forward and as an aid to making progress through thick cover for yourself.

DO Stay where you are told if on stop.

DO Make sure that you fully understand your instructions and the direction in which you are heading.

DO Wait for the signal to start a drive.

DO Keep an eye on the keeper for instructions during the drive.

DO Keep in line and evenly spaced.

DO Obey instructions such as moving forward or waiting back if told or signalled to do so.

DO Pass messages if asked to do so.

DO Keep in touch with beaters either side, by voice, if working in thick cover and they are out of sight. It is very important that there should be no gaps in the beating line that the birds can escape through.

DO Kill any wounded birds as quickly as possible, preferably by hitting on the head with your stick.

DO Use your eyes - look for birds that may be skulking in the cover.

19.2 A Picker-up with birds and dogs

Beaters Dont's

DON'T Be rude to either guns or the keeper.

DON'T Swear loudly in line - voices carry a considerable distance.

DON'T Move out of the allotted area if you have been left as a stop.

DON'T Shout loudly - especially near the heading of a drive - the tapping of a stick provides sufficient noise.

DON'T Bring a dog unless requested to do so.

DON'T Work a dog if it is not steady.

DON'T Walk around the edge of thick cover - you are employed to go through it.

DON'T Go beating if you are not interested in what you are being paid to do.

Pickers Up Do's

DO Arrange to come with the keeper's knowledge.

DO Arrive punctually.

DO Enquire whether picking up during a drive is approved of or not.

DO Check before the start of a day which drives are being shot and if there are any areas that you or your dogs must not go in.

DO Get in a position to mark wounded or dead birds that fall at a distance behind the guns.

DO Make sure that the guns are aware of your position, unless you are sufficiently far back as to be out of range.

DO Work as a team with the other pickers up.

DO Keep your dogs on a lead if they are not steady or cannot be trusted to walk to heel between drives.

DO Mark birds accurately and be prepared to spend some time searching.

DO Remember to provide your dogs with fresh drinking water, if there is none naturally available.

DO Search the area immediately behind the guns. Often they are not able to pick up every bird though they possess dogs.

DO Inform a gun that you have picked up a bird if there is the possibility of him sending his own dog.

DO Remove the collar, especially a choke chain, from your dog before working it.

Pickers Up Dont's

DON'T Bring any dog that is not properly trained, especially if it will not retrieve properly.

DON'T Bring a dog that is consistently hard mouthed.

DON'T Deliberately send two dogs for one bird.

DON'T Let your dogs run about near the guns while a drive is in progress.

DON'T Waste time picking up dead birds with your dogs that can easily be gathered by hand.

DON'T Hover around the guns unless specifically requested to stand close, such as may be necessary when partridge or grouse shooting.

DON'T Make a lot of noise either by shouting or continuous use of the whistle.

DON'T Kill wounded birds by swinging them by the head.

DON'T Pick up any birds that the guns may wish to send their own dogs for.

DON'T Send your dog out on ice.

Guns Do's

DO Be punctual and make sure how to reach the arranged venue.

DO Arrive properly dressed and with sufficient cartridges. Enquiries may be made beforehand as to the kind of day planned.

DO Stay on the peg number you are given unless given specific instructions to do otherwise.

DO Keep your dog tethered if it is not perfectly steady.

DO Make sure you are fully aware of the position of fellow guns, stops, and pickers up.

DO Mark the position of runners or distant birds accurately and be sure that pickers up or the keeper is informed.

DO If possible leave some object (e.g. spent cartridge or broken branch) to indicate position of shot game not picked up.

DO Pick up any dead birds near to your peg and carry them back to the transport. If they are left beside your peg inform the game cart man that they are there.

DO Tip the keeper. It is often the only reward he gets for the long hours he puts in. Overtime is seldom paid.

DO Be sure your gun is unloaded between drives.

DO Remain sober at lunchtime.

Guns Don'ts

DON'T Shoot greedily or in a manner that is unsafe.

DON'T Be rude to fellow guns - any problems that arise should be dealt with by the shoot organiser.

DON'T Swing your gun through the line; it is very dangerous to point a loaded gun at anyone, including beaters.

DON'T Wear light coloured or shiny clothing that may deter birds from coming in your direction.

DON'T Make a lot of noise when taking up positions for a drive.

DON'T Leave gates open.

DON'T Claim to have hit a bird knowing that it has been clean missed. Much time and energy of man and dog is wasted looking for such birds or birds that are claimed by two guns, when in fact one has been shared.

DON'T Kill game by holding it by the head and swinging it around. The body may become detached when the bird is tied and either hung up or carried.

DON'T Bring a dog that is noisy or unruly.

DON'T Ask a picker up to the shoot without the approval of the keeper.

DON'T Interfere with instructions issued to beaters or stops.

DON'T Attach a dog's lead to yourself; it is exceedingly dangerous.

20

Glossary ofAbbreviations,

Shooting Terms

and Others

A

AIR GUN   Type of rifle from which the pellet is propelled by compressed air.

ALARM GUN   A trip wire device that fires a blank cartridge, used as a poacher deterrent.

ANTI Member of an organisation or person against all forms of bloodsports.

ASPERGILLOSIS   Respiratory disease of game birds caused by a fungal infection.

AVIARY   Term sometimes used to describe the communal pen in which breeding stock is kept.

B

BAG   Term used to describe the total number of game shot.

BAIT   Food used to entice or lure.

BARREL   Tube through which ammunition is discharged from a gun.

BARREN   Without young.

B.A.S.C.   British Association for Shooting and Conservation (Previously WAGBI).

BEAT   A prescribed area of a shoot or river.

BEATER   Person employed to drive game.

B.F.S.S.   British Field Sports Society.

BIT   A small plastic or metal device fixed into the nostrils, and laying between the upper and lower mandibles, to prevent feather pecking in pheasants or partridge.

BLANKING IN   A Manoeuvre in which a cover is driven into another, but is not shot.

BLEEPER   Electronic device fitted to the collar of a ferret or a terrier so that its precise position under the ground may be located from the signals emitted.

BLACKHEAD   Protozoal disease of game birds.

BLACK NECK   A normal coloured pheasant; the cock birds do not possess a white ring of feathers around the neck.

BLIND   A hide, a place in which to conceal oneself.

BOHEMIAN   A pale, sandy coloured strain of pheasant.

BORE   The dimension of a gun barrel.

BOX LOCK   The design of the mechanical working part of a shotgun.

BRACE   Two dead game birds that are tied together. If possible a cock and a hen.

BRAIL   Strap made from tape or leather for securing a bird's wing in such a position that it cannot fly.

BRASH   Trim the lower branches from a tree.

BROOD   Number of chicks accompanying a parent bird.

BROODER   A device to provide heat for young chicks.

BROODY   A hen or bantam in a state where she will incubate eggs or care for chicks.

BRUSHING   Norfolk term for beating.

BUCK   Male rabbit, fallow deer or roe deer.

BULLET   Ammunition for a rifle.

BUTT   A hide or place in which to conceal oneself.

BUTT   The end of the stock of a gun.

C

CABINET SETTER   Large incubator in which paddles or a fan is used to circulate warm air.

CALIBRE   Dimension of the interior of a rifle barrel.

CANDIDIASIS   Disease of game birds in which a fungal infection affects the crop (MONALIASIS).

CANDLE   Shine a strong light through an egg to check fertility or the size of the air cell.

CANNABALISM   A vice when young game birds peck each others flesh.

CARTRIDGE   A paper or plastic case containing lead shot used as ammunition for a shotgun - BLANK CARTRIDGE is one containing no shot.

CATCHER   A cage constructed from wood, wire netting or weld mesh, that is used for catching game birds without harming them.

CATCHING UP   Term used for trapping wild game birds for the laying pen.

CHARLIE   Term used for a fox by the hunting fraternity.

CHIP   A stage of hatching at which the chick begins to peck its way out of the egg.

CHOKE   The tapering of a gun barrel.

CHOKE LEAD   A slip lead, a running noose used for restraining a dog.

CHUKAR   Hybrid French partridge. A foreign species of partridge which has been crossed with French partridge to produce a hybrid.

C.L.A.   Country Landowners' Association.

CLAY   A small disc launched into the air for practice or competitive shooting with shotguns.

CLEAR   Term used to describe an infertile egg.

CLIP   Term used to describe the cutting off of some of the primary wing feathers.

CLUTCH   Number of eggs laid by one hen.

COCCIDIOSIS   Disease of game birds caused by a protozoal infection.

CONTACT THERMOMETER   A Thermostat used in some incubators that is accurate to .1 of a degree.

COURSING   Hunting by sight - one or more dogs in the act of chasing (usually hares).

COVER or COVERT   Area of woodland or other crop which will harbour game.

COVEY   Brood or group of partridges or grouse.

C.P.S.A.   Clay Pigeon Shooting Association.

CYMAG   Lethal white powder which emits cyanide gas when exposed to air and moisture. Used for destroying rabbits, rats and foxes underground.

D

DE-BEAK Remove tip of upper beak with clippers or heated appliance to prevent feather pecking.

DECOY Imitation animal or bird used to lure or entice. The act of using imitations or the dead of a certain species to attract the attention of others.

DIDDICOY Gypsy.

DOE Female rabbit, fallow or roe deer.

DOGGING IN The act of using a dog to chase pheasants away from shoot boundaries or other unwanted areas.

DOUBLE BANK Place a team of guns in two lines, one behind the other.

DOUBLE GUNS Two guns used by an individual to shoot. A loader is employed to re-load.

DREY The nest of a squirrel.

DRIVE An area designated to be shot.

DRIVING IN Chasing pheasants or partridges away from boundaries, etc., to prevent straying.

DULL EMITTER Heating device that emits no light.

DUMMY Canvas covered or similar object used to teach dogs to retrieve.

DUMMIES Artificial eggs.

DUN Stage in the development of a fly.

E

EARTH Holes in which foxes live.

E. COLI An abbreviation given to a type of bacterial disease that affects game birds.

EGG EATING Vice in breeding stock when the eggs laid are eaten.

EGG TOOTH A blunt spike on the tip of the upper beak which is used by a chick to chip its way out of the shell. It drops off within a few days of hatching.

EJECTOR A shotgun with a built-in device that ejects empty cartridges automatically when the gun is opened.

ELECTRIC HEN Type of brooder that provides warmth by contact.

ENTER Term used when a terrier is introduced to working underground.

E.S.S. English Springer Spaniel.

EUSTON SYSTEM   A system of wild partridge management by which eggs in the nest are picked up and substituted with dummy eggs. They are incubated artificially and returned to the sitting bird when due to hatch.

F

FEATHER PECKING   Vice that occurs when birds pull out each others feathers.

FENN   Type of spring trap.

FERAL   Domestic creature that is living wild.

FIELD TRIAL   A trial held under simulated shooting conditions to test a dog's working ability.

FLAG   A flag made out of material, or more often plastic, that is used to channel game birds in the desired direction when used by beaters.

FLANK   The outside edge of the beating line.

FLIGHT   The movement of birds to and from feeding or roosting areas.

FLIGHTING   Shooting of birds, particularly wild fowl, when flying naturally.

FLOCK MATING   System of management whereby breeding stock are kept in a communal pen.

FLUSH   Term used to describe the moment when a bird rises into the air. Often used when a great many birds rise at the same moment.

FLY   An unbaited hook decorated to represent an insect.

FLY TYING   The art of making a fly as described above.

FOREND   The wooden part of a gun that is fixed beneath the barrels.

FORE SHORE   Area of coastline between the high and low water marks.

FOWL PEST   Virus disease of poultry that may affect game birds, also known as Newcastle Disease.

F.T.CH. or F.T.W.   Abbreviations to denote a dog has been judged either Field Trial Champion or Winner.

FUMIGATION   The destruction of bacteria, etc. by the production of a gas.

G

GAFF   A hook for landing large fish.

GAME BOOK   Book in which a record is kept of game shot.

GAME CART   Trailer adapted so that freshly shot game may be hung up and transported.

GAME COVER   Crop grown specifically to harbour game.

GAME LARDER   A place where freshly shot game is hung.

GAPES   Parasitic disease of game birds caused by the presence of worms in the bronchial tube (SYNGAMIASIS).

GHILLIE (GILLIE)   A Scottish term used for an assistant to a stalker or a fisherman.

GIBBET   A line where dead vermin is hung and displayed.

GIN   An illegal spring trap with teeth-like jaws.

GRALLOCK   Term used for gutting a deer.

GREY   Grey Partridge or English Partridge.

G.S.D.   German Shepherd Dog (Alsatian).

G.S.P.   German Shorthaired Pointer.

GUN   Term used to describe a person shooting.

GUN SHY   Term used when a dog is terrified of the noise of a gun being fired.

GUN STAND   Clearing cut to allow vision for a standing gun.

G.W.P.   German Wirehaired Pointer.

H

HALF GUN   Member of a syndicate who shoots on only half the shoot days and subscribes accordingly.

HARD MOUTH   Serious fault in a retriever; the act of biting game.

HATCHER   Incubator used for the final stage of hatching.

H.D.   Hip Dysplasia - an hereditary defect found in some breeds of dogs.

HEAD   The antlers of a deer.

HEAD (TO)   Position chosen for the conclusion of a drive.

HEXAMATIASIS   Protozoal disease of game birds.

HIDE   Place in which to conceal oneself.

HIND   Female red or sika deer.

HOB   Male ferret.

HOPPER   Container used to store and dispense feed so that access is available at all times.

HOT   Term used to describe a dog that is overkeen and difficult to handle.

H.P.R.   Abbreviation for Hunting, Pointing and Retrieving. A breed, such as the German Shorthaired Pointer, which is expected to perform all three aspects of gundog work.

I

IMBRA   Type of spring trap

INFRA RED LAMP   Heat emitting bulb used for rearing game birds.

J

JILL   Female ferret.

JUBY   Type of spring trap.

JUG or JUK   Term used when a pheasant chooses to sleep on the ground instead of going to roost in a bush or tree.

K

K.C.   Kennel Club.

KICK   Recoil of a gun when it is fired.

KIT   Young ferret.

L

LAMPING   Hunting or shooting at night using the beam of a lamp.

LEAD   The distance allowed in front when shooting at a moving object.

LEFT AND RIGHT   Consecutive hits with both barrels of a shotgun.

LINE   Scented trail left by an animal or bird.

LINER   A ferret that is worked attached to a length of cord.

LLOYD   Type of spring trap.

LOADER   Person employed to load guns or gun of person shooting.

LOCK   The mechanism for firing a gun.

LONG DOG   A lurcher.

LONG NET   A length of net stretched across gateways or such, into which the quarry is driven.

LURCHER   A fast running dog, often a crossbred, that is used to catch hares (or illegally game or deer).

M

MAGAZINE   A device for storing and automatically dispensing ammunition.

MARK (TO)   To make a mental note of the spot that shot game or any thrown object has landed.

MELANISTIC A strain of black pheasant.

MONALIASIS See Candidiasis.

MOOR Area of moorland where grouse are shot.

MULE Pheasant that shows characteristics of both sexes.

N

NET Term used for a pouch net that is placed over the hole to trap bolting rabbits or fox, when working ferrets or terriers.

NEWCASTLE DISEASE See FOWL PEST.

NYMPH Stage in the development of a fly or the dressed hook imitating it.

O

OGRIDGE Hybrid French partridge.

OPEN REARING FIELD Old fashioned system of rearing, using broody hens and coops.

OVER & UNDER A shotgun with one barrel placed on top of the other, most commonly used for clay shooting.

P

PACK A large number of grouse.

PATTERN   Distribution of pellets from a cartridge when fired from a shotgun. Tested at certain distances on a metal plate.

PAUNCH Remove intestines from a rabbit.

PEG Numbered stick indicating where a gun must stand during a drive.

PEG (TO) Term used when a dog catches unshot game.

PHOSTOXIN Compound of aluminium phosphide in tablet form used for gassing rabbits, rats and moles.

PICK UP Term used for the collection of dead or wounded game.

PICKER UP Person employed to pick up (as above) with dogs.

PIKEY Gypsy.

PIPPING See CHIP.

POST MORTEM (PM)   Examination conducted to establish cause of death.

POULT Juvenile game bird.

PRA Progressive Retinal Atrophy - Hereditary disease causing blindness in dogs.

PRICK Lightly hit by shotgun pellets.

PRIEST Small heavy instrument used to kill fish or game.

PROOF A stringent safety test on the barrels of a shotgun to prove that they are strong enough to withstand firing. Proof marks are small symbols stamped on the barrels denoting that they have been passed.

PUNT GUN Large crude gun mounted in a flat boat for shooting wildfowl.

PURSE NET See NET

R

RED LEG French Partridge.

RIFLE A gun that fires a single bullet a long distance with great accuracy. The single barrel is grooved inside so that the bullet spirals.

RING NECK A normal coloured pheasant; the cock birds have a white ring around the neck.

RISE Term used when a fish breaks the surface of the water.

ROD Term used for a person who fishes.

RODING The territorial flight of a woodcock.

ROOST Perch on a branch at night.

RUN Track used regularly by an animal.

RUNNER Wounded game bird that is unable to fly.

RUNNING Term used when a wild animal is particularly active.

RUN IN Term used when a dog chases or retrieves without waiting for the command to do so.

RUPERT Type of brooder for rearing game.

RUT The mating season for deer.

S

SET (TO) To commence the incubation of eggs.

SETT   Holes in which badgers live.

SETTER   Incubator used for the first stage of incubation until eggs are transferred to the hatcher.

SEWELLING   Length of string to which strips of material or plastic are attached which is used to prevent pheasants from running past a certain point.

SHOTGUN   A gun with one or two smooth barrels that fires cartridges containing lead pellets for a relatively short distance.

SIDE BY SIDE   Shotgun with two barrels side by side.

SIDE LOCK   Design of the mechanical working part of a shotgun. Superior in quality to the box lock.

SITTER   Term used to describe a hen bird that has begun to incubate eggs.

SLEEVE (TO)   Renew gun barrels.

SLIP   Carrying case for a gun.

SLUG   Pellet for an air rifle.

SNARE   Hoop of wire made into a noose to catch foxes, rabbits, etc.

SNICK   Sound, similar to a sneeze, made by a bird suffering from gapes.

SOFT MOUTH   Term used to indicate that a dog can retrieve game without causing any damage to it.

SPEX   Plastic device inserted into the nostrils that prevent egg eating and feather pecking.

SPINNER   A lure for catching fish, or a fully matured fly.

SPUR   Sharp growth on the back of a cock bird's leg.

SQUEAK (TO)   Mimic the squeak of a frightened rabbit in order to entice vermin within shooting range.

STAG   Male red or sika deer.

STEADY   Term used to describe a dog that remains under control.

STEDDLE   Roof of straw beneath which corn is fed to pheasants.

STEW PONDS   Large outdoor tanks used for rearing fish.

STILL AIR   Type of incubator often used for hatching. Air is circulated by convection.

STOCK   The wooden part of a gun that fits into the shoulder.

STOP   Person employed on a shoot day to prevent pheasants straying.

STRONGYLOSIS   Parasitic disease of partridge and grouse.

SYNDICATE Team of guns who subscribe to the annual cost of running a shoot.

SYNGAMIASIS See GAPES.

T

TEALER Length of stick that supports a snare in the correct position.

TELESCOPIC SIGHT An instrument mounted above the barrel of a rifle to magnify the target.

TOBY Term used for a fox.

TOWER (TO) Term used to describe the action of a bird that has been shot, when it rises upwards in flight before falling.

TREADING The act of mating between birds.

TROPHY Term used to describe exceptional quality, usually applied to fish or the antlers of deer.

TUNNEL A small passage constructed from any naturally available material in which to set a trap for small animals.

V

VELVET The soft velvet-like skin that covers the antlers of deer during growth.

VENISON The meat of deer.

VENT The back passage of a bird.

VENT PECKING Vice of pheasants which lead to cannabalism.

VERMIN Term used by gamekeepers for any species of creature that is harmful to game.

VIXEN Female fox.

W

WAGBI WIldfowlers Association of Great Britain and Ireland now renamed B.A.S.C.

WALKING GUN Gun who walks with or behind the beaters during a drive.

WARFARIN An anti-coagulant poison used for the control of rats and grey squirrels.

WHELP (TO) The act of giving birth by a bitch - sometimes the name given to a newly born puppy.

WILD   Term used to describe a dog that is uncontrollable.

WING TAG   A clip inserted into the loose skin at the front of the wing for the purpose of identification.

WORKING TEST   Artificial test conducted to assess the obedience and control of a gun dog under simulated shooting conditions.

WRY NECK   Condition existing in young reared pheasants in which the neck appears to be bent to one side.

Y

YOLK SAC   Unabsorbed yolk that remains inside the body of a newly hatched chick.

YOLK SAC DISEASE   Bacterial infection in very young chicks caused by entry through the shell of the egg prior to hatching.

APPENDIX :

Useful Addresses

B.A.S.C.
British Association for Shooting and Conservation,
Marford Mill, Rossett, Wrexham, Clwyd LL12 0HL.

G.C.
The Game Conservancy, Fordingbridge, Hampshire SP6 1EF.

B.F.S.S.
British Fields Sports Society, 59 Kennington Road, London SE1 7PZ.

C.P.S.A.
Clay Pigeon Shooting Association, 107 Epping New Road, Buckhurst Hill, Essex IG9 5TQ.

C.L.A.
Country Landowners Association, 16 Belgrave Square, London SW1X 8AB.

M.A.F.F.
Ministry of Agriculture, Fisheries and Food, Headquarters, Whitehall Place, London SW1A 2HH.

M.A.F.F. Publiations
Willowbarn Estate, Alnwick, Northumberland NE66 2PF.

The British Deer Society
Church Farm, Lower Basildon, Nr. Pangbourne, Berkshire RG8 9NH.

The Game Farmers Association
Hon. Secretary: S.H. Jervis Read, CBE, MC., The Cottage, Little Chart, Near Ashford, Kent.

Sparsholt Agricultural College
Sparsholt, Near Winchester, Hampshire.

Shooting Times and Country Magazine
10 Sheet Street, Windsor, Berkshire SL4 1BG.

R.S.P.B.
The Royal Society for the Protection of Birds, The Lodge, Sandy, Bedfordshire.

INDEX

A

Air Rifle - 262, 323, 324
Aspergillosis - 162

B

Badger - 67, 312
Beaters - 26, 185, 341, 343
Black Grouse (Blackcock) - 193
Blackhead - 163
Brooders - 95, 112, 114, 115, 117
Broodies - 89, 91
Buzzards - 51

C

Canada Goose - 207, 208
Candling Eggs - 86, 87
Candidiasis - 162
Capercaillie - 193
Cartridges - 253, 255
Cat - 5, 52, 301
Catching Up - 72, 76
Chicks, Care of - 89, 91, 95, 97, 99
Chinese Water Deer - 239, 253
Coccidiosis - 163
Coli Septicaemia - 159
Conditions of work - 10-12
Conservation - 4, 212
Coot - 49
Coypu - 53
Crow - 47

D

Deer - 53, 233, 243, 245, 330, 331
Dogs - 53-55, 173, 244, 301, 318
Driving Grouse - 201
Driving Partridges - 184
Driving Pheasants - 26, 27, 143, 145
Driving in - 128

E

E. Coli - 159
Eggs, care of - 79, 160
Electric Fence - 150
Euston System - 180

F

Fallow Deer - 236, 239
Feather Pecking - 124, 168
Feeding - 79, 104, 110, 122, 124, 1\26, 132, 185, 201, 212
Ferrets - 267, 269-271
Fishing - 219, 224, 226, 333, 334
Flags, use of - 185
Flighting - 21, 212, 213
Fowl Pest - 158
Fox - 8, 55, 56, 196
Fox Hunting - 82

G

Gadwall - 210
Game crops - 143, 151-154
Game Laws - 325, 326
Gapes - 165
Gas - 38, 57
Goldeneye - 210
Golden Plover - 211
Grayling - 218, 333, 334
Greylag Goose - 208
Grouse - 191, 198, 199, 201
Grouse Disease - 166, 199
Guard Dogs - 173, 297, 317
Gun, care of - 212, 258
Gun, development of - 250, 253, 254
Gun, safety - 249, 250, 258
Guns, placing of - 26, 145
Gundog, breeding of - 292, 293
Gundog, care of - 282
Gundog - choice of - 278, 280
Gundog, training of - 284, 286, 288-293

H
Habitat - 139, 141, 177, 178
Hare - 57, 59, 325
Harrier - 51
Hatching - 87, 89
Heaters - 112, 114, 115
Heather - 194, 316
Hedgehog - 59
Hexamitiasis - 164

I
Incubators - 82, 86, 87

J
Jackdaw - 49
Jay - 49

L
Loading - 259

M
Magpie - 49
Mallard - 208, 213, 313
Marble Spleen Disease - 159
Mink - 61
Mole - 61
Moniliasis - 162
Moorhen - 49
Muntjac Deer - 239
Myco Plasmosis - 160

N
Newcastle Disease - 158
Night Shooting - 63, 327

O
Owls - 51

P
Panic - 168
Partridge, English - 76, 79, 177-182, 185, 187
Partridge, French - 76, 79, 177, 187
Picking up - 294, 295, 343, 344
Pigeon - 51, 52
Pink Footed Goose - 208
Pintail - 210

Pheasant - 15, 72, 76, 79
Poaching - 149, 171-174, 224, 236, 328, 329, 332
Pochard - 210
Poisons - 35, 38, 61, 66, 167, 309-311
Police - 171, 301
Predator control - 17, 31, 33, 35, 38, 178, 196, 198, 222
Protozoa - 163
Ptarmigan - 191
Punt Gun - 262, 263
Puppies - 280, 282, 293

R
Rabbit - 61, 63, 269, 270, 324, 326
Rat - 63
Rearing, Duck - 112, 118
Rearing, English Partridge - 112, 117, 118
Rearing, French Partridge - 112, 117, 118
Rearing, Pheasants - 91, 95, 97, 99, 110-112
Red Deer - 236
Releasing, Duck - 132, 314
Releasing, English Partridge - 128, 132, 184, 314
Releasing, French Partridge - 128, 314
Releasing, Pheasants - 104, 122, 124, 148, 149, 314
Rifle - 261, 262, 320-324, 331
Roe Deer - 239
Rook - 50

S
Salmon - 218, 219, 333, 334
Salmonella - 160
Sewelling - 143
Shoot Days - 7, 24, 25, 27, 184, 185, 199
Shot Guns - 253-258, 319, 320, 323, 324
Shoveler - 210

364

Sika Deer - 239
Snares - 40, 309, 312
Snipe - 210, 214
Sparrow Hawk - 51
Sprays - 4, 67, 150, 178
Squirrel - 64
Stalking - 243, 244
Starling - 50
Stoat - 66
Stress - 166
Strongylosis - 166, 199
Syngamiasis - 165

T

T.B. (Avian Tuberculosis) - 161
Teal - 210
Terriers - 57, 196, 296, 297
Thrush - 162
Traps - 42-46, 309-311
Trichomoniasis - 164
Trout - 218, 219, 222, 224, 228,
229, 333, 334
Tufted Duck - 208, 210

V

Vermin - see Predator Control

W

Walking up - 201
Water Insects - 226
Weasel - 66
Weather - 25, 145, 179, 182,
198
Wigeon - 210
Wildfowling - 211, 212
Wildlife and Countryside Act -
302
Woodcock - 17

Y

Yolk Sac Disease - 162

RECENT LEGISLATION

The following changes are lkely to be enforced when the *Firearms (Amendment) Act 1988* becomes law.

Many shotguns will be controlled by Section 1 of the existing *Firearms Act.* These include a) those with barrels less than 24 inches in length or less than 40 inches overall length, b) every shotgun which has a detachable magazine, (c) shotguns with non-detachable magazines unless the magazine is limited to a capacity of two shots. (If it is necessary to convert the gun, then it must be re-proofed).

Shotgun certificates will become more difficult to obtain. The Chief Officer of Police will now have the power to reject the application if he is not satisfied that the applicant can be permitted to possess a shotgun without danger, etc. A shotgun certificate shall be granted unless the police are satisfied that the applicant does not have good reasons for possessing one. Fees for certificates are likely to rise considerably.

There will also be statutory security conditions concerning the safe keeping of shotguns. The owner will also be required to report the number of shotguns in his possession as well as descriptions and identification numbers and to provide details of disposals and acquisitions.